To Mellisa

From Matin Carel

MCC

THINNER, FITTER, *Happier*

DANCING WILL CHANGE YOUR LIFE!

MARIAN C. CONDON

This book is designed to provide information on dancing only. Readers should consult a physician in matters relating to health and particularly with respect to any symptoms that may require diagnosis or medical attention. The author and publisher shall have no liability or responsibility to any person or entity regarding any loss or damage incurred, or alleged to have incurred, directly or indirectly, by information contained in this book.

Year of the Book
Glen Rock, PA 17327
yotbpress.com

ISBN 13: 978-1-942430-12-4
ISBN 10: 1-942430-12-4

Library of Congress Control Number: 2015932389

Acknowledgments

Three years ago, I walked into an Arthur Murray studio in York, Pennsylvania. I didn't know the staff and community of dancers at that studio were going to change my life, but they did. I will never be able to thank them enough. Never, ever.

I'm also tremendously grateful to the more than forty dancer-interviewees who welcomed me into their homes and studios and shared their passion for the magnificent art that enhances their lives as it does mine. Some confided moving and inspiring stories of personal transformation and transcendence. Others enlightened me about dance communities that, while substantially different from mine, are similarly nourishing and rewarding. Still others filled me in on how the business side of dancing – which makes the social side possible – works.

I'm also most grateful to my editor, John DeDakis. John is a former senior copy editor at CNN, a successful author, and a terrifically nice guy. Check him out at JohnDeDakis.com.

My pal, Mike Stambaugh – who was REALLY paying attention in English class – skillfully netted errors that somehow made it past John and me. Big hug, Mike.

Big hug also to shutterbug (and dancer) extraordinaire, Anton Marx. Anton snapped some excellent headshot pictures of interviewees located in his geographic area.

Seasoned ballroom dancers Bill and Cindy Scullion, featured in interviews AND videos, brought me up to speed on the intricacies of ballroom competition. Thanks, guys.

Finally, this book would not have made it into print, and onto Amazon, without Demi Stevens and Year of the Book Press. Author, writing guru, and publisher, Demi is truly the Wonder Woman of

Words. I learned more about the craft of writing in her classes than in my thirty years as a college professor. Love ya, D.

And finally, a big *Thank you!* to the multi-talented (ballroom teacher, musician, and graphic artist) Oscar Restrepo,who designed the book's very appealing cover.

Dedication

This book is dedicated to dance teachers everywhere – instructors, coaches, and studio owners. You bring your students joy. You inspire us with your knowledge and hard-earned skills. You make the enormous benefits we derive from dancing possible.

Thank you.

⌇

This book is also dedicated to the wonderful instructors at my studio, Arthur Murray Central Pennsylvania. With your energy, enthusiasm, and big smiles, you make every class, and every party, fun…and you put up with *me* with amazing grace.

Thank you.
I love you.

⌇

But most especially, this book is dedicated to my primary teacher, Tim Hippert. Without your authentic warmth and caring, your innate verve and flair, your quick and sometimes naughty wit, your implacable persistence – and preternatural patience – I doubt what I've called my Arthur Murray Miracle would have occurred.

Know you make a difference. *Know* what you do matters.

Thank you.
I love you.

Table of Contents

GETTING DOWN WITH THE TRIBE: THE STUDIO AS A THERAPEUTIC ENVIRONMENT

EVERYTHING YOU DIDN'T KNOW ABOUT SOCIAL DANCE

Introduction

I wrote this book because dancing changed my life and I want you to consider the possibility that it could change yours. When I started doing social partner dancing at an Arthur Murray (A.M.) studio three years ago, I was 60 pounds overweight and in not-so-great physical shape. Divorced and without a romantic partner, I watched two to three hours of television every night to keep myself occupied. On weekends, I headed out to mediocre movies just to have someplace to go. I was also a recreational eater. Forking down the rich foods I loved and discovering new restaurants were the most enjoyable activities in my life.

Predictably, I had high blood pressure, along with borderline-high levels of blood sugar and LDL (bad cholesterol). As a Registered Nurse on the wrong side of sixty, I knew I was setting myself up for serious health problems down the road, but felt powerless to change my lifestyle. I'd been a yo-yo dieter for years and had tried many weight-loss programs – Atkins, Weight Watchers, Nutrisystem – all to no avail. Pounds I'd lose initially would always creep back. And they'd bring friends. I had to have clothes to accommodate the three weight categories through which I endlessly cycled: saint, sinner, and OMG!

With a library of health and fitness books, I knew part of my problem was a reluctance to exercise. Few people can keep weight off without exercising, but I could not find anything I could stick with for long. I'd tried walking and running and strength training. They were physically uncomfortable or just plain boring. My basement was crammed with idle exercise equipment. I'd dropped out of the gym nearest me so many times I was ashamed to go back.

If you're thinking to yourself, *That poor soul*, you misunderstand. Before I took up dancing, I was not consciously suffering or even unhappy. Yeah, I felt bad about my weight and had a horrible body image, but in general, I had what most people would consider a good life. I had a satisfying job, great relationships with my two phenomenal sons, a nice place to live and friends I could count on. I was a published author, laughed a lot, and if asked, would have described myself as content.

Yep, I had a good life – ok, a *very* good life – but I did not have a GREAT life. From time to time I found myself channeling Peggy Lee and asking, *"Is that all there is?"*

I was aware, particularly when alone and without distraction, that a certain *joie de vivre* was missing. While I was marching briskly through life, I wasn't doing much *skipping*. I was interested and occupied but not *jazzed*. I attributed my ever-so-slight malaise to being chronically overweight and ashamed of it. I didn't feel attractive. I despaired of ever finding another romantic partner. In short, I was in a state author/speaker Mario Martinez calls *comfortable misery* – I had resigned myself to a life devoid of a major turn-on of any kind. I was free of conscious suffering only because I had become numb to my boredom. Then the gods sent an Arthur Murray Groupon to my inbox and everything changed.

In the pages that follow, I will tell you how partner dancing changed my life physically, emotionally and socially. I'll tell you how I lost over 60 pounds and got into better shape. And I'll tell you how dancing threw some sort of happy switch in me – it fired up my circuits in a way I still don't fully understand. My teacher, Tim Hippert, henceforth referred to as T.H. – short for *The Hottest* (dance instructor in the world) – thinks what turned me on was passion...my newfound passion for dance. While I think T.H. is partially right about that (we will explore the nature and significance of passion in Chapter 6) I think another powerful joy-producing factor, the *Tribe*, was also involved. By the Tribe, I mean my dance community – my fellow students at Arthur Murray, and of course, the teachers.

Emotion is contagious. If you go among people who are mourning, you will start to feel sad. Conversely, if you walk into a dance studio and place yourself among people who are listening to music, dancing, and having a great time, you will take on the group's positive vibe. You will forget, temporarily, whatever negativity may exist at home or work.

Stay tuned for more about the Tribe and testimonials from fellow dancers who attest to its power.

Speaking of testimonials, I will introduce you to other dancers whose lives have been changed as much, or more, than mine. For example, you'll meet Harvey, who was warned by his doctor that he was heading for a stroke. Harvey took off more than 45 pounds and – now that he can rumba like a Latin King – enjoys the confidence and *panaché* of the handsome young naval officer he once was. You'll meet Ricardo, who took off an astonishing 110 pounds, and Kevin, who, cripplingly shy when I first met him, is now a self-assured and outgoing master of West Coast Swing. Perhaps most inspiring of all, you'll meet John, a dapper 97 year-old who attributes his sharp mind and limber body to the intricate ballroom patterns with which he still challenges himself.

You'll also hear from quite a few ladies – Beth, who lost weight and got her mojo back as I did, and Becca – a no-nonsense satellite engineer who still marvels at her ability to transform herself into a glittering Ballroom Queen. And, you'll meet Amanda, Kristin, Carline, and JoAnn, whose respective dance communities serve as both lifeline and refuge. Along the way, I'll tell you what science has to say about the surprising benefits of dancing, and theorize about why the Terpsichorean art has proven such a powerful elixir for so many people.

I'll also outline the various styles of dance from which you can choose if you decide enhanced health and happiness are reasons to give something new a try. I'll fill you in on Ballroom, which is studio-based and focuses on dances such as Waltz, Foxtrot, Rumba, Cha Cha, (aka Cha-Cha, ChaCha, Chacha & even Cha Cha Cha) and many more. I'll also tell you about the major "street" dance styles popular with the large communities of people who, while not necessarily associated with a studio or club, keep up with teachers, dance venues, and competitions via Facebook and the Internet.

Finally, I'll introduce you to some of my personal heroes – the dance instructors and studio owners who create the magic that is social dance. And (bonus!) you'll find out what will be involved should you decide to challenge yourself at competitive and exhibition dance events.

Dancing

Will Change

Your Body

1

I'm Not Fat Anymore

...our weaknesses, whatever their nature, are each the secret seed of a new strength unlike anything imagined in our unending dream of overcoming what now defeats us. ~Guy Findley

You already know I've lost over 60 pounds since desperation drove me to dancing about two years ago. In a nutshell, I was fat because I was an emotional eater addicted to foods that made me feel good, temporarily, and because I also hated exercise.

Sugar Addiction

I used to be actively addicted to sweets, particularly the starchy kind – anything made out of flour, fat and sugar. Like most addicts, I was ashamed of my habit and tried to hide it. I would indulge in a donut or piece of cake only when alone or in the presence of a fellow overweight person. And like most addicts, I was able to quit baked goods for short periods of time, but would quickly relapse because doing without them made me feel so bad. Research published in 2007 suggests sugar is as hard to quit as cocaine. Yes, I said *cocaine*. Scientist Magalie Lenoir and her team found when lab rats had a choice between eating sugar and receiving an intravenous dose of cocaine, they tended to choose sugar. [1]

Even more astonishingly, when rats addicted to cocaine were allowed to choose between getting another hit and eating sugar, they chose the sugar.

What makes sugar so powerful?

Both cocaine and sugar trigger our brain to synthesize and release dopamine, one of the body's major feel-good chemicals. When we ingest sugar or introduce cocaine into our body, the brain gets a signal to produce dopamine, in a more or less dose-dependent manner, and we experience pleasure.

The researchers who conducted the rat-sugar-cocaine study theorized that our taste buds, which evolved when our distant vertebrate ancestors had access to very little sugar, are not really equipped to handle the relatively large doses most of us now take. When stimulated by a high-sugar food, our taste buds send signals to the brain that trigger a comparatively huge dopamine response that makes us feel so wonderful it can override our self-control mechanisms and lead to a type of addiction. Whatever the actual mechanism, the bottom line is that once your body has adjusted to receiving frequent, heavy doses of sugar, withdrawing it will cause a sharp decline in your dopamine levels…and your mood.

What allowed me to get my addiction under control was discovering an alternate source of the good feelings sugar so reliably produced. I now get my highs from some alchemical combination of my passion for Ballroom, endorphins (the body's natural opiates) generated by dancing and all forms of exercise, and the contagious joy with which I am regularly infected by the Tribe. I now have a blood

---

[1] Lenoir M, Serre F, Cantin L, Ahmed SH (2007). Intense sweetness surpasses cocaine reward. PLoS ONE 2(8): e698. doi:10.1371/journal.pone.0000698

pressure well within normal limits and an LDL on which I've been congratulated by my doctor.

People ask me regularly what I did to take the weight off and what I have to do to keep it off, and I imagine you'd like to know, too. Here's the short version of that story, starting with how I came to be an emotional eater – a person whose food consumption is driven more by the mind than the body – in the first place.

You Have Fat Ankles

I was an only child. Unfortunately, my mother was afflicted with bipolar disorder, aka manic-depressive psychosis, and started to become symptomatic when I was about 11 years old. If you know anything about mental illness, especially untreated mental illness, you know life was complicated for my dad and me from that time on.

I turned to sweet foods for solace and distraction and the pounds accumulated slowly, over the years. By the time I hit middle age, I was noticeably overweight and felt really guilty about it. In the house in which I was raised, being fat was seen as sinful.

Both my parents had been slim when I was growing up – my mother had even done some modeling – and my father remained so throughout his life. He was messianic about exercise and self-control around food.

And he was a relentless appraiser of women's bodies.

I remember well the day he looked me over and said, "Don't worry about those fat ankles. They'll slim down as you get older." Fat ankles? Up to that point, I'd not given my ankles much thought. Looking down as he spoke, I thought, *'What fat ank...? – Oh.'*

Not long after that, a boy at swim club favored me with his own observation about my body: "Your thighs are fat," he said.

Looking down once again, I could only plead guilty as hot shame burned its way from my cheeks to my heart.

No wonder the scale has had way too much power over me since pre-adolescence: if my weight was down, I'd feel euphoric and virtuous, but if it was up, I'd be filled with self-recrimination.

Thus was the cycle in which I remained mired for many years...until dancing came along.

It took me about a year and a half to lose 60-plus pounds and acquire the sleek bod I'd wanted my whole life. People ask me often what I did to lose the weight and how I keep it off. Simple: I sold my soul to the devil. Kidding!

Losing It

My actual strategy, after some trial and error, was as follows: I bought an inexpensive little book called *CalorieKing*, by Allen Borushek, and started a food diary in which I kept daily track of every morsel I put in my mouth and the number of calories it contained. I'd learned from experience I couldn't eat more than about 1,100 calories a day if I wanted to shed pounds, and limited my intake accordingly. Eleven hundred calories isn't much, particularly for a woman as tall (5'8") as I am.

I used to suspect years of yo-yo dieting had slowed my metabolism, but according to experts, that's not the case.[2] Perhaps I should blame my grandmother instead.

The emerging field of *Epigenetics*, Latin for *above genetics*, suggests that our predisposition to a host of problems and ailments may be linked not only to our own lifestyle but to the circumstances of our forebears' lives, including what they ate and whether they were well-loved as children.

Epigenetics is like classical genetics' younger, hotter, and mysteriously beguiling sister.

Epigeneticists look not only at genes themselves, but at factors that determine whether a given gene or gene cluster is on or off. Genes that are turned *on* are active; they direct the body to make specific proteins, which are the building blocks of our anatomy and critical to many of our physiological processes. Genes that are turned *off* are dormant, at least temporarily, and thus irrelevant to the body's processes.

---

[2] O'Connor, A. (2005). The claim: Repeated dieting slows your metabolism. New York Times Health. Downloaded from http://www.nytimes.com/2005/05/17/health/17real.html?_r=0

Epigenetic research has uncovered the paradigm-shifting fact that *environmental factors*, both internal and external, determine whether most of our genes are turned on or off. Active or passive. Dormant or life-changing.

The circumstances of our lives – where we live, what we eat, how clean our air is, the manner in which we relate to people, whether we perceive our job as stressful – constitute our *external* environment. Our thoughts and feelings are our *internal* environment.

Early epigenetic research focused on the outer environment. The findings were mind-boggling.

For example, adding a certain ingredient to a pregnant mouse's diet prevents her pups from inheriting a trait normally transmitted genetically.[3]

Moreover, diet is not the only external factor that affects genes' on-or-off status. For better or worse, nurturing in infancy and childhood also plays a role.

Moshe Szyf, a scientist at McGill University, found that rat pups that had been well-licked by their mothers grew up to be less easily frightened and calmer overall than pups born to less conscientious moms.

Szyf went on to find that in rats, licking activates genes that affect the brain in ways that foster a muted, as opposed to robust, response to potentially stressful experiences and circumstances.

Heads-up, moms! Your pediatrician may soon be urging you to give your kids a good licking![4]

As in rats, so in people. A study done at Kaiser Permanente Hospital in collaboration with the Centers for Disease Control and Prevention[5]

---

[3] Watters, E. (2006). DNA Is Not Destiny: the new science of epigenetics rewrites the rules of disease, heredity, and identity. *Discover Magazine.* Downloaded from http://discovermagazine.com/2006/nov/cover.

[4] You can access a *trés* cool video on Szyf's incredibly important work here: http://learn.genetics.utah.edu/content/epigenetics/rats/

[5] Middlebrooks, J.S., Audage, N.C. (2008). The effects of childhood stress on health across the lifespan. National Centers for Disease Control and Prevention. Atlanta: GA. Downloaded from http://www.cdc.gov/ncipc/pub-res/pdf/childhood_stress.pdf

found that individuals who experienced childhood stress because of dysfunctional parenting have more physical and mental health problems as adults than similar individuals whose parents were free of alcoholism and mental illness and did not engage in domestic violence.

Perhaps epigenetics' most amazing revelation is that it is possible that one of my grandmothers – or grandfathers – actually did have something to do with my near life-long battle of the bulge.

According to information presented in the Public Broadcast System video *The Ghost in Our Genes,*[6] it seems that if

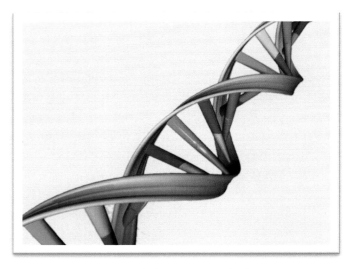

you are male, and your grandfather was well-fed as a boy, as opposed to having experienced famine, your chances of developing diabetes during your lifetime are *quadrupled.*

While we can do nothing to change our forebears' experiences, most of us have a tremendous amount of control over our own. Are you aware that identical twins, who share almost exactly the same genes, die ten years apart, on average?

According to Dawson Church's riveting book, *The Genie in your Genes,* the reason boils down to lifestyle – differences in the twins'

---

[6] Watch the *The Ghost in Our Genes* video at: http://topdocumentaryfilms.com/the-ghost-in-our-genes/

respective inner and outer environments. People who are optimistic, happy, peaceful, altruistic, and genuinely spiritual simply do better, physically and mentally.

The outer environment is important, too. No doubt you're up to speed on the importance of clean air and water and healthy food. I do want to point out, however, that, according to the somewhat imposing *Handbook of Social Psychology*, by Dan Gilbert, the quality of the relationships we have with other people is tremendously important to our psychological and physical health.

For example, the degree to which we perceive ourselves as having access to *social support* (emotional and tangible assistance from others), has been found to have a more powerful effect on our health than what we eat. Moreover, it's not just the actual assistance itself that matters. The perception that help is *available* also makes social support a powerfully protective factor.

Another aspect of our external environment that deserves our attention is *stress*. Avoiding people and circumstances that cause us to feel stressed is an excellent health-promoting strategy. When we live and work in a constant state of anxiety, our stress levels rise and we feel trapped. When we surround ourselves with positive and happy people, our stress levels decline and our outlook on life improves.

If you think, as I once did, that the most stressed-out folks among us are likely high-powered executives and other types with heavy schedules and a lot of responsibility – you're wrong.

Research done originally in baboons by neuroscientist Robert Sapolsky, and later in humans by Gary Sherman and his team, indicates that it's not the high-ranking apes and people who are most likely to be stressed, but their *subordinates*.

Dominant baboons chivy their underlings relentlessly, causing high levels of stress hormones to be released into subordinate baboons' blood. The situation is not all that different in humans. As long as one has sufficient authority, responsibility is not particularly harmful. It's *responsibility in the absence of power* that sets the stage for emotional and physical illness – particularly in a scenario that includes a toxic boss.

Back to my favorite topic – me – and how I lost weight.

In addition to counting calories, I also weighed myself every day. I'd come to an important realization. My scale was not only a vengeful accuser, it was also a tremendously useful biofeedback device. In combination with my food diary, it showed me exactly how the foods I'd eaten over the last day or two affected my body.

I learned that if I consumed more than very limited amounts of starchy, highly-refined carbohydrate foods such as pasta, bread, cake, donuts, etc., I could expect to see a higher number on the scale within two days, even if I'd stayed within my caloric allotment.

That's because for every gram of carbohydrate we consume, we retain about 3 grams of water![7]

Carbohydrates, including those contained in fruits and veggies, are stored in the body as glycogen and the glycogen-forming process requires water. A double whammy is that carbs also cause the body to retain sodium – and sodium causes water retention. Happily, fruits and veggies also contain generous amounts of the mineral *potassium*. Potassium helps the body release sodium, thereby preventing fruits and veggies from causing water-retention.

> ## DID YOU KNOW?
>
> We retain about 3 grams of water for every gram of carbohydrate we consume.

Those baked goods that held me in their thrall, however, had no such mixed effects. They contained not only starchy, sugary, water-retaining carbs but plenty of actual sodium as well – a blueberry donut from Dunkin' Donuts, for example, contains *570 mg.* of sodium.

Speaking of water retention, bloat – particularly in my lower extremities – has always been a major problem for me. Both of my parents had prominent varicose veins in their legs and I inherited a full complement of bad vein-valve genes.

Even though I'd had some of the faulty vessels removed back in my 40s, my ankles still swelled unattractively if I traveled for any length of

---

[7] McKittrick, M. (2012). Why does your weight fluctuate so much? Downloaded from http://citygirlbites.com/blog/archives/9209

time by car or airplane. I recall walking the streets of Cairo, Egypt, accompanied by my then-husband, with ankles so swollen they ballooned out over the tops of my shoes.

> ## DID YOU KNOW?
>
> Dinner plates are 20% larger today than in 1920.

When I first started dancing, water-retention issues required me to wear heavy support hose to limit swelling in my lower extremities. Thankfully, revamping my diet has made that much less of an issue for me. As long as I'm eating healthily, I can dance for hours in regular hose without a problem.

I do have to take precautions when staying at hotels for dance events, though. Restaurant food tends to be salty, so I put on my support hose and stick with salads, cooked veggies, lean meats, fish and fruit, and take a pass on the pastas, soups, sauces, breads, rolls, biscuits and desserts.

Another thing I did when I was losing weight – and do still – was eat only foods I really like. I've learned the hard way that I just won't stick to an eating plan if I can't enjoy my meals.

Fortunately, I don't have a big appetite now. I eat pretty much anything I want (aside from the aforementioned pasta, bread, rolls, etc.), but in small portions. I find it no longer takes as much food to satisfy me.

Many of us eat much more than we really need; restaurant servings are now enormous and we've become accustomed to having a lot of food heaped onto our oversized plates. Did you know dinner plates are 20% larger than they were in 1920?[8]

I eat relatively small amounts at any one time – a typical lunch is half a sandwich on bread made from sprouted grains (fewer carbs and more protein) and some soup or cut-up fruit. If I start to feel hungry between meals, I'll have a snack, often a protein shake. I always take healthy food to work with me.

---

[8] http://www.divinecaroline.com/self/wellness/portion-size-then-vs-now

If I'm in the car and realize I'm famished, I'll stop at a fast-food joint, order a burger or a broiled chicken sandwich, toss the white-flour bun and eat the protein. I try never to let myself get really hungry when away from home, because that's when I tend to hit restaurants – places best avoided if you want to be slim.

The family restaurant and fast-food industries have made a science of getting us hooked on food that's bad for our waistlines and health. They know how to combine fat, salt and sugar into foods so delicious they are, for all intents and purposes, addicting. Also, restaurant food is *salty* and I stay away from salt for the same reason I avoid refined carbs – water weight.

Another tool I used to lose weight – and keep it off – is something called Official, or Gold Standard, *Emotional Freedom Techniques (EFT)*. EFT is a treatment modality within the field of energy psychology and can be thought of as emotional acupuncture. Rather than using needles, EFT practitioners tap on acupuncture points with their fingertips while simultaneously focusing on a particular target: a problematic or painful belief, attitude or emotion. The tapping creates changes in the energy system and brain which neutralize the target and prevent it from influencing, often outside conscious awareness, our decisions and behavior. I used EFT to uninstall from my mind the belief that permanent weight loss was impossible for me.

I also used it to short-circuit food cravings.

Recently, I'd been traveling, and therefore forced to dine in a series of restaurants. In one of them, I spied in a dessert case a round éclair slathered with fudgy icing and sliced in half – its creamy center fully exposed. The near-pornographic succulence of the image almost did me in. I knew *exactly* how the thick swath of rich chocolate would taste as it melted on my tongue and could almost *feel* my teeth crunching through the puff pastry shell on their way to the custardy decadence within. I very nearly succumbed to that éclair but EFT saved me. I used the tapping protocol while focusing on each of the confection's irresistible attributes, one by one, until all had lost their power.

Over 50 clinical trials have been conducted on EFT to date. EFT has been found effective in lessening or banishing a wide range of difficulties. It is thought to work by weakening the ability of targeted thoughts and memories to activate arousal centers in the brain. Gary Craig, who developed the original (it's been much-imitated) form of EFT over 20 years ago, has made extensive information on the topic available at no cost to the public. I've become certified in Gary's Official, Gold Standard EFT and am teaching others how to use it to improve their lives.[9]

Over the past couple of years, EFT has helped me weaken my food addictions to the point where I actually

> **DID YOU KNOW?**
>
> EFT can help you eliminate food cravings and self-defeating habits.

prefer light, healthy foods to the rich, heavy ones I used to crave. I'm still a sugar junkie, though. Addictions don't go away. The best you can do is control them.

Occasionally, I'll hear the siren call of one of my old faves and decide to indulge. I have strict rules about that, though. If I didn't, one donut would lead to another and I'd soon be watching the numbers on my scale creep upward.

The first rule is that if I'm going to eat a dessert, I don't eat it on *top* of the meal. I eat it *instead* of the meal. I'll order soup or salad and then have the delicacy *du jour* as my entrée.

The second – and perhaps most crucial – rule is that I don't purchase whole cakes or pies and bring them home. My doing that would be tantamount to a recovering alcoholic buying a fifth of scotch. If I decide to flirt with one of my demons, I don't invite it up to my place for a drink. I make sure the rendezvous takes place in a restaurant or someone else's home.

---

[9] Learn more through Gary Craig's www.emofree.com, and www.DrMarianCondon.com

2

Dancing: Exercise That Doesn't Suck

No one loses weight and keeps it off without exercising. The physicality of Ballroom – it's very aerobic – had a lot to do with my initial weight loss and helps me maintain it. Think about all the huffing and puffing you see on *Dancing with the Stars*.

Researchers who studied the energy expenditure of professional Ballroom competitors characterized it as *heavy to extremely heavy*.[10] They said dancing at that level is comparable to playing basketball or running cross-country.

Even at the much lower level at which I perform, dancing definitely burns calories. Moreover, all forms of dance build muscle, which spurs weight loss. Muscle tissue performs work. It burns calories at a slightly faster rate than fat tissue does.

As I started to get into better shape from dancing, I became more willing to pursue other forms of exercise. I started walking a lot and jogging a little, and gradually became more fit. I would share my small triumphs with T.H. and he would rejoice with me – even though telling him I could run a mile was like telling Lance Armstrong I could make it all the way around the block on my bike.

Remember, I'd tried walking and running before, and always wound up quitting. Since the joy-switch was thrown, however, I've been able to stick to my exercise program. Other dancers, such as Beth and

[10] Blanksby, P.A. & Reidy, P.J. (1988). Heart rate and estimated energy expenditure during ballroom dancing. British J. of Sports Medicine.

Harvey – whom you'll meet shortly – have also experienced that phenomenon. Now, I actually look forward to going to the park for exercise.

Note that I said *park*, not gym. While I know many people like gyms – more power to them – I don't. I've discovered that for me, the ticket to converting exercise from a chore to a joy is walking/running outdoors in nature with upbeat music that makes me feel really alive blasting through my ear buds. The tunes rev me up and trigger a starburst of happy associations in my brain. More about that in a later chapter.

While the *combination* of the park setting and the music allow me to enjoy exercise, I've found that one without the other doesn't do it. Perhaps, as both being in nature and listening to music are known to have positive effects on our physical and mental health, my experience is due to some sort of fortuitous synergy.

Being outside in nature is good for humans, both physically and mentally. Studies show running or walking in a green, natural area (as opposed to on a treadmill or road), decreases levels of anger, anxiety, and depression. Nature is our real home. It's where we evolved.

Nature is indeed *Mother Nature*.

Her proximity confers benefits. Her grandeur is uplifting and inspiring. People who live relatively close to parks or other large, wooded areas are less likely than people living farther away to suffer from anxiety and depression.[11]

I'm grateful that I have a magnificent, 750-acre park nearby in which I can rev up my body while simultaneously restoring my soul. I've even been known to practice dance moves on flat sections of trail, if I think no one is around. I get caught sometimes – and the only consequences thus far have been bemused smiles and the occasional question about what sort of step I'm doing.

The strategies and practices described above helped me do what I needed to do in order to lose weight and keep it off. I want you to remember, though, it was *dancing* that flipped my joy-switch initially

---

[11] Louv, R. (2012). Health benefits of being outdoors. AARP Bulletin. July 23rd.

and readied me for physical rebirth. Want more proof that Merengue or Mambo just might work similar miracles on your bod? Here's what Beth Driscill, a business woman who's been dancing for only six months at a studio in Texas, has to say:

Beth: *Last fall, I came to the realization that I needed to end my long marriage. I knew I would have to get stronger in order to do what needed to be done, so, at the beginning of the year, I made a commitment to treating my body the way I should.*

There is an Arthur Murray studio in my town, near a major interchange, and for years, I have been watching folks twirl around behind the big glass windows and thinking, "I would love to do that!" So, long story short, I started dancing at the end of January.

I have almost completely stopped eating the evil white things like sugar and flour – one of the best things I have done for myself! I've also taken up spinning and other fitness endeavors and have lost 35 pounds since January. I don't think I could have stuck to it without Ballroom.

Carline Coleman cares for her mentally disabled adult son at home. Carline dances at an Arthur Murray studio in Severna Park, Maryland, and has also seen improvement in her physical health:

Carline: *I enjoy it because it's good for my health, mentally and physically. I was under a lot of* *stress, I'd been diagnosed with borderline diabetes, and my blood pressure was high.*

I'm so much better now. I still take a little bit of medication for my blood pressure, but my doctor says I'm doing fine. And my weight has gone down about 10 pounds.

I found out I have muscles in my ankles. I was walking through the mall one day and I felt this pressure under my ankle strap and I looked and I saw this little muscle sticking out. I didn't know I had muscles in my ankles!

My legs have gotten stronger, my calves. Before I started dancing, I'd go to my doctor and my ankles would be swollen, but that doesn't happen anymore.

Dancing has made me want to take care of myself...I eat better...I've gotta look good in my gowns, my pants, everything! I sure don't have to wear a girdle anymore. I don't feel 60. I feel like I did when I was 40.

Bill Scullion, and his wife, Cindy, have also lost weight. Bill is a retired military officer and attorney who is now a civilian consultant to the Department of Defense. Cindy is a tax-preparer and accounting firm co-owner. They dance at Arthur Murray studios in Pennsylvania and Florida:

Bill: *Cindy lost 40 pounds through going to a gym and eating better. Her body is more supple and has more curves. She's more confident. More comfortable.*

I'm beginning to get there, too. I weigh about 20 pounds less than I did; I used to hate to look in the mirror. At one of the competitions, I saw an instructor who's heavier than I am and he was moving his butt off, and I said to myself, "OK, you have no excuse. It's not what your body looks like, it's what you can do with it." You find parts of your body you don't even remember ever using in your life.

Anton Marx, a businessman, dances with his realtor wife Cherella, at the Arthur Murray studio in Severna Park, Maryland. Anton and Cherella have advanced to the coveted gold level in ballroom dancing. Anton credits his years of dancing for having saved his life:

Anton: *I've had two heart attacks. My doctor told me I'd be dead now if I wasn't dancing.*

The reason Anton's doctor believes Anton's dancing saved his life has to do with his coronary arteries and the collateral circulation that likely developed in them.

The coronary arteries are blood vessels that supply the heart muscle with the oxygen and fuel it needs to keep pumping 24/7. They are rather small in diameter to begin with, and if plaque starts to build up in one of them, it can become completely blocked.

When a coronary artery is totally occluded, the part of the heart muscle it normally supplies with blood is deprived of oxygen to the point where it dies. That's a heart attack.

Happily, people who get regular exercise often have more than one vessel supplying blood to a given area of the heart. If one vessel is blocked, others will still function and no death of heart muscle will occur.

Harvey Swoboda is a Vietnam vet who dances at Arthur Murray York, Pennsylvania, with his wife, Karen. Harvey is a speech therapist and Karen is an occupational therapist. Harvey is well on his way to regaining the pride and panache he once enjoyed as a handsome young naval officer:

Harvey: *I've lost 45 pounds. I've gone from a 50 waist down to a 35 waist.*

We just started to eat differently. We used to go to a restaurant and we'd each order dessert along with a third to take home. Now we eat mainly soups and salads, and if we want dessert, we split one. I'm not really driven by food anymore.

You asked if dancing had anything to do with that. Well, as a scientist, I look for the one thing that has changed in our lives...and what changed is that we took up dancing.

When I first came to the studio, I was not a fit person; I was sick. There were many things that were just going bad.

Now my blood pressure and my cholesterol and my other numbers are much better. They just keep on going down.

Am I really trying to change the way I eat? No. I'm taking this as an experiment – seeing if dancing will just change me without any effort on my part other than showing up at the studio. And it has. It is.

I don't even want to eat the way I did.

My expectation is that I'm going to pretty much get back to what I could do when I was in my twenties. I'm already much stronger.

In the beginning, I would put my left hand up to start dancing, and after a while, it would just slowly start to droop down, and then the rest of me would droop down, because everything was weak.

And now, I can just move and move. I can do the hustle for 15 minutes and not get a sweat. And my posture and balance are just so much better now.

The most astonishing tale of Terpsichorean transformation was shared by "Ricardo Fabuloso." R.F. is the pseudonym of a silver 2-level dancer who has been doing Ballroom for nine years. Ricardo writes the honest, funny and sometimes angst-ridden ballroom blog *Facing Diagonal Wall*.[12] I knew from R.'s blog that dancing has done a lot for him and that he's lost a substantial amount of weight, but I didn't know *how much* until our conversation.

Me: Ricardo, you've mentioned on your blog that you've lost a significant amount of weight since you started dancing. How much have you lost?

Ricardo: One hundred and ten pounds.

Me: Wow! Congratulations! That's awesome! And I know from the blog you've kept it off – that's even more awesome.

Ricardo: I've kept it off for over a year now.

Me: How long did it take you to lose the weight?

Ricardo: About a year.

Me: What was it about dancing that motivated you to lose weight?

---

[12] Visit Ricardo's blog at: http://diagonalwall.wordpress.com/

Ricardo: *I enjoy competitions and showcases, but my wife doesn't, so when I first started to compete, I would be dancing with this much younger, much thinner person [his instructor] and I was the blob standing next to her. I hated that.*

Also, at some point in this journey, it became important to me not just to do Ballroom, but to do well at it. So I started focusing more on technique. And then I had to take a look at what was holding me back. And the weight was holding me back.

There's nothing worse than going to a showcase and getting all dressed up, and halfway through the first Viennese Waltz, you're sweating like crazy. And then you're uncomfortable for the rest of the day.

I couldn't finish a lesson without breaking into a sweat. I would look at videos of myself and I would think, "This is awful. I just can't handle this." That was about two years ago. I just decided it was time.

Me: *How did you approach losing the weight? What did you do?*

Ricardo: *I didn't go full Atkins, but I cut starchy carbs way down. We changed the way we cook, too. We eat more vegetables now.*

One of the challenges was portion control. In the past, we'd cook something and there'd be four servings. My wife would eat one of them and I'd eat the other three. Now we don't cook as much food.

And I started to get more exercise in addition to dancing. Once I started to lose some weight and develop more stamina, I joined the gym at work. I still hit the treadmill pretty much every day now. I did 55 heats at the last showcase.

Weight loss and conditioning are not the only better-body bonuses dancing has to offer. Dancing also yields better balance, stronger bones and muscles, and improved posture.

The Better Balance, Better Bones & Mo' Muscle Boogie

Balance was a major issue for me when I first tried to follow T.H.'s graceful movements across the floor. Especially when it came to turning. I simply could not execute underarm turns well because I would wobble on the way around. I'm happy to report that while not perfect, my balance is now much better, as are my turns.

I'm by no means the only dancer who has noticed that dancing improves balance.

Miss Mary Green is a 76-year-old retired family and child services counselor. She lives near Severna Park, Maryland, and has been dancing for four years at the Arthur Murray studio there. Miss Mary had this to say about what her hobby has done for her:

Mary: *Dancing has made me more graceful. I've lost 40 pounds and a lot has toned up. My balance is better...some of the steps we had to do, I could hardly keep my balance. And also, I have sciatica, and that's so much better. My doctor says, "Keep on doing what you're doing."*

The evidence that dancing improves balance is not only anecdotal. Ten weeks of Tango has been found to enhance coordination and balance in healthy seniors aged 68-91.[13]

Dancing has even been found to improve balance in patients suffering from neurological injuries and diseases. In the course of a study carried out in Ottawa, Canada, dancing improved balance and

---

[13] McKinley, P., et al.(2008). Effect of a community-based Argentine tango dance program on functional balance and confidence in older adults. *Journal of Aging and Physical Activity*, 16(4), 435–453.

coordination in a group of brain-injured people more than participation in a standard exercise program.[14]

Parkinson's disease is a serious neurological condition that interferes tremendously with mobility. Researchers at the Washington University School of Medicine found that after only 13 weeks of classes in Tango – what is it about *that* dance?? – persons suffering from Parkinson's had improved their balance and ability to walk forward and backward.[15]

Dancing is, of course, a weight-bearing activity and thus supports bone mineral density and bone strength. And, it's not as hard on the joints as high-impact sports such as running. Having good balance and strong bones is of major importance to everyone, but especially to older people such as Miss Mary, because falling and landing on a brittle hip can add up to a one-way ticket to a nursing home…or worse.

Physician-researcher Erin LeBlanc followed a group of women 65 and older who had fallen and broken a hip, and also followed a similar group of ladies who had not. Dr. LeBlanc found the ladies in the hip-fracture group had a much greater chance of dying within the next year.[16]

Falls in general are a tremendous threat to older people and are less likely to occur if balance and coordination are good and ankle muscles strong…all benefits conferred by dancing.

---

[14] Berrol, C.F., Ooi, W.L., & Katz, S.S. (1997). Dance/movement therapy with older adults who have sustained neurological insult: A demonstration project. American Journal of Dance Therapy, 19(2), 135–160.

[15] Hackney, M., Kantorovich, S., & Earhart, G. (2007). A study on the effects of Argentine tango as a form of partnered dance for those with Parkinson's disease and the healthy elderly. American Journal of Dance Therapy, 29(2), 109–127.

[16] Wyckoff, W.B. (2011). A quirky picture for risk of death after hip fracture. Downloaded from http://www.npr.org/blogs/health/2011/09/27/140837746/a-quirky-picture-for-risk-of-death-after-hip-fracture

Speaking of muscles, scientists report that starting at age 50, the average person loses muscle at a rate of about 1-2% per year.[17] This progressive muscle loss is known as *sarcopenia*. Sarcopenia is not your friend. Unless you do something to prevent it, it will cause you to lose 30% of your muscle mass by the time you've reached age 70. If you allow yourself to become progressively enfeebled, you will have difficulty rising from a chair and carrying groceries.

The steady loss of musculature is one of the main contributors to looking, acting and feeling old. That this insidious process is not inevitable is illustrated by a video titled *Mathilda's Solo.*[18]

The video shows 94-year-old Ballroom competitor Mathilda Klein dancing quickstep, dubbed *quick* for a reason, with her instructor, Danny Malony. Dancing has helped Ms. Klein maintain muscle tone and strength in her lower body and her all-important *core* – the trunk-support muscles located in the lower back, abdomen and pelvis.

---

[17] Chantal Vella and Len Kravitz. Sarcopenia: The mystery of muscle loss. http://www.unm.edu/~lkravitz/Article%20folder/sarcopenia.html

[18] Watch the Mathilda Klein video at: http://youtu.be/8LOdmka4_90

Dancing Will Set You Straight: Better Posture

Ah, posture. Perhaps because I'm a tall woman, I've had a lifelong tendency to slouch. I can remember my parents nagging me to stand up straight when I was young.

A few years ago, a public speaking coach warned me I was sabotaging myself by not holding my head up and standing tall. He said how we carry ourselves directly influences how we are perceived by others. When we stand tall and straight, we convey an air of authority, confidence, and competence. When we slouch, we appear indecisive and ineffective.

The field of *Embodied Cognition* – how the body influences the nature of the human mind – takes that concept further. It conceptualizes thought not as an isolated phenomenon that takes place in the brain, but as a *system* that functions simultaneously in the brain, the body and the surrounding environment.

This hypothesis is based on a rapidly expanding body of research[19] that suggests our thinking patterns are influenced by the ways in which we interact physically with our environment. The act of looking upward prompts us to call to mind others more powerful than ourselves, while looking downward has the opposite effect – we think of people less powerful. Our body even seems to influence the way we see the physical world. When volunteers were asked to estimate the steepness of a hill, those who were in good physical condition perceived it as less steep than did volunteers who weren't as fit.

While it is premature to claim embodied cognition is *the* reason or even one of the reasons people tend to gain self-confidence as they progress in dance, the possibility cannot be ruled out.

Dancing will improve your posture – guaranteed. When I first showed up at Arthur Murray, T.H. was on me about that immediately – "Head up! Head up!" he would exhort, always pleasant, but relentless. While I had resented my parents' efforts to get me to straighten up –

---

[19] McNerney, S. (2011). A brief guide to embodied cognition: why you are not your brain. Downloaded from http://blogs.scientificamerican.com/guest-blog/2011/11/04/a-brief-guide-to-embodied-cognition-why-you-are-not-your-brain/

diplomacy was not my mother's strong suit – I understood T.H. was trying to help me and so I tried hard to please him. The authority and presence his own impeccable carriage conveyed was persuasive. He shared that in his pre-Arthur Murray days, he, too, had been a sloucher, and that gave me hope.

Nevertheless, years of stooping made standing up really straight for any length of time painful. The muscles in my upper back had weakened while the pectoral muscles in my chest had become tighter and resistant to being stretched. It took almost a year of constant effort, in and out of the studio – and the assistance of a chiropractor – to strengthen my back muscles and open up my chest to the point where standing tall became easier and felt more natural.

While I haven't heard "Head up! " for a while, I still sometimes get a subtle signal – a discreet upward tilt of the instructorial chin – that I'm backsliding, posture-wise.

Virtually everyone who takes up dance winds up standing taller. One of the questions I asked the more than 40 people interviewed for this book was "Has dancing improved your posture?" and the answer

was always "Yes." Such was the case with Don and Cheryl Youtz, who have been dancing for 11 years at Top Hat Studio, which has locations in Leola and Philadelphia, Pennsylvania:

Don*: I have more confidence in myself. I carry myself better.*

Cheryl*: My daughter says I walk like a dancer – my shoulders are back, my tail is tucked and my head is up. My back problems are much better now. Your muscles get stronger.*

Remember "Ricardo Fabuloso," the intriguing mystery man who lost over 100 pounds after he took up dancing? Ricardo has also benefited from the erect carriage dancing confers:

Ricardo: The emphasis on posture has helped me make more connections and relate to people better. I walk around all day now trying to keep that posture where it's supposed to be – to walk with my back straight and my head up.

And I've found that when your head is up, you're looking at people as they're walking toward you. I'm an introverted person, and I used to always walk around with my head down, but now, my head is up, and I naturally make eye contact with people.

I'm much more likely to say "Hi" to them now, and maybe get a conversation started. I manage a group of people, and they respond to me better as a boss, now that they know me as a person.

Dancing

Will Change

Your Brain

3

Remember This!

Dancing will affect your brain as profoundly as your body. Regardless of whether a person is leading or following, dancing stimulates the brain enormously.

Dancers have to stay on rhythm while executing complicated steps and patterns, often rapidly. They must also maintain constant physical communication with their partner and avoid collisions with other couples.

Dancing provides an incredible amount of stimulation to the senses, particularly sight, hearing and touch. It also places great demand on what is known as *proprioception* – our ability to know where our body is located in space.

Happily, as the brain is struggling to factor all this input into the lightning-fast decisions it must make about how the dancing body needs to move, it is getting regular blasts of oxygen. As mentioned earlier, dancing can be a highly aerobic activity.

The demands dancing places on dancers' brains have positive implications for their memories.

It is well-known by biologists that after age 50 or so, an area of the brain called the *hippocampus* starts to shrink. Typically, it does that at a rate of about 0.5% a year. Your hippocampus is where information from short-term memory is transferred to long-term storage. A badly shrunken hippocampus makes Jack a dull boy. You want to do everything you can to preserve yours.

Exercise is one of those things.

When scientists studied the (living!) brains of older adults who agreed to walk for 45 minutes, three days a week, for a year, they found that by the end of the study, the size of their subjects' hippocampi had *increased* by 2%. [20]

So, even if you've already begun having more senior moments than you'd like, don't assume you can't reverse that trend. Your memory, like other functions of your brain, can be toned up just as surely as your biceps.

Note the seniors in Kramer's study increased the size of their hippocampi by merely *walking*. Had they been engaging in partner dancing, and subjecting their brains to its extreme demands, they may well have ended up with hippocampi that were positively bulging.

Carline Coleman reports that dancing has sharpened her thinking:

Carline: *I was forgetting things, but now, I'm sharper – much quicker. My brain just changed.*

Kevin Sand, a pharmacy technician who dances at Arthur Murray York, Pennsylvania, believes dancing has enhanced his concentration:

---

[20] Courage, K.H. (2011). Aerobic exercise bulks up hippocampus, improving memory in older adults. Downloaded from http://blogs.scientificamerican.com/observations/2011/01/31/aerobic-exercise-bulks-up-hippocampus-improving-memory-in-older-adults/.

Kevin: I'd definitely say dancing has improved my ability to concentrate. You have to focus so hard on some of those [dance-related] things. For leading, especially.

You gotta hear the music… you gotta think three steps ahead in terms of what you want to do [patterns] and where you want to go…and not run the lady into the wall or into another dancer.

And if the floor is crowded, it's like, 'Oh no! Here comes someone…oh, dear God…what am I gonna do??' Sometimes it's just so difficult…but it builds you and it helps you.

Anton Marks, whom you met earlier, is in his late sixties and believes it is his dancing that allows him to continue to be a force to be reckoned with at work:

Anton: I know people my age who are not physically active and it's like their world shrinks a little more every year. They have no new ideas or interests. They're just marking time. In contrast, I am the oldest person in my company; I compete with kids who are right out of college, in their early twenties – people in their thirties and forties – and I do, I would have to say, by my standard and theirs, as good a job as I did ten or twenty years ago.

I work efficiently and solve problems.   Without the constant intellectual challenge [of dance], I think the nimbleness that allows me to look at a bunch of fuzzy circumstances and arrive at a solution, would slow down to the point where I couldn't function in that job anymore. But I have no way of proving that…and I don't want to experiment!

Anton may well be correct in attributing his mental agility to dance. According to a study done by Dr. Peter Lovatt, a British ballroom dancer and scientist, partner dancing enhances one's ability to engage in *divergent* thinking.[21] Divergent thought allows us to perceive multiple possibilities for solving a given problem. That dancing is absolutely fabulous for the brain has been documented by other researchers as well. Read on.

---

[21] Tucker, I. (2011). Peter Lovatt: "Dancing can change the way you think." Downloaded from http://www.theguardian.com/technology/2011/jul/31/peter-lovatt-dance-problem-solving.

4

Dancing Away from Demon Dementia

Developing Alzheimer's Disease, or some other form of dementia, is something most people past middle age think about and fear. We know few of us will escape it entirely. We will either fall victim to it ourselves or watch a loved one in its implacable grip descend slowly into that heartbreaking fog from which there is no return. Fortunately, there is evidence dancing has the potential to save us, at least from the former.

Researchers at the Albert Einstein College of Medicine found that social dancing conferred a greater degree of protection against Alzheimer's than *any other leisure activity.*[22]

The study that revealed this astounding benefit was longitudinal. That means individuals studied were followed over a long period of time – 21 years, beginning when they were 75 years of age or older. They kept a diary of leisure activities and their level of cognitive functioning was evaluated periodically.

People in the study reported engaging in a wide variety of mental and physical pursuits: reading, writing for pleasure, doing crossword puzzles, playing cards, playing musical instruments, playing golf, playing tennis, swimming, walking for exercise, doing housework, and, of course, dancing.

---

[22] Ingram, T. (2013). Dancing makes you smarter? How dancing may prevent dementia. Downloaded from http://www.bboyscience.com/dancing-prevents-dementia/.

Dancing yielded the *highest* level of protection against Alzheimer's Disease and other forms of dementia. Moreover, it was the only physical pastime that yielded *any* level of protection. Here's how the various activities (when performed frequently) scored:

Activity	*Dementia Risk Reduction*
Bicycling	0% reduction
Swimming	0% reduction
Golfing	0% reduction
Reading	35% reduction
Working crossword puzzles at least four days a week	47% reduction
Playing board games	74% reduction
Dancing	**76% reduction**

If those results won't get you to leap into your car and burn rubber to the nearest studio, I don't know what will. Maybe all those fitness places should be offering *Cha Cha and Chess* sessions instead of Zumba!

The reasons seniors who dance frequently enjoy a significant degree of protection against dementia is likely because dancing places demands on the brain that stimulate it to grow new neurons and sprout new neural connections.

In college, I learned the brain couldn't make new neurons but that has been proven false; it can and does. Neuroscientists now know the brain is actually the most rapidly modifiable structure in the body. Changes can often be measured within a matter of hours!

An example of the brain's prodigious *plasticity* (a medical term that means moldable) is its ability to adapt to extreme physical alteration. If the entire left-hemisphere of a young child's brain is removed – a drastic procedure done only to manage intractable epilepsy – the child will still be able to learn and use language. The surviving right-hemisphere will take over the language-processing function.

Like the rest of the body, the brain operates on the use-it-or-lose-it principle. A frequently-challenged brain tends to function well, even as we age. Its plentiful supply of neural cells and circuits allows it to better withstand the ravages of diseases such as Alzheimer's longer than could a less lavishly-wired organ.[23]

According to Dr. Steven Brown's 2006 research on what goes on in the boogying brain, dancing gives our gray matter a heck of a workout.[24] Brown used a medical procedure known as functional imaging to study the parts of dancers' brains that got activated when they took to the floor. The results were impressive.

Both sides of the dancers' brains lit up (displayed telltale colors on the scanner) at the same time, which is excellent news. When the left and right hemispheres are in sync, *integration* is said to be present, and hemispheric integration is known to support learning – something we want to remain good at as we age. Dancing was also found to activate areas of the brain responsible for motor control, sensory integration, spatial image processing, mental focus, and memory.

No wonder dancing confers such marvelous protection against dementia. The use-it-or-lose-it principle applies just as surely to mental processes as it does to muscle.

Here are some other brain-related tidbits you may want to keep in mind. Being overweight *doubles* your risk for developing Alzheimer's

---

[23] For a well-thought out reflection on the implications of the study that identified dancing as an antidote to dementia, and some practical suggestions as to how to get the maximal brain-boost out of dancing, see Professor Richard Powers' article, "Use It or Lose It: Dancing Makes You Smarter," available at http://socialdance.stanford.edu/syllabi/smarter.htm?mid=56.

24 Brown, S. (2011). Is dance the "next wave" in cognitive neuroscience? Downloaded from http://www.psychologytoday.com/blog/the-guest-room/201111/is-dance-the-next-wave-in-cognitive-neuroscience

Disease. Being obese (having a body-mass index greater than 30) *triples* it.[25]

Both high blood-pressure and diabetes will accelerate the rate at which your hippocampus shrinks over time.

Still not convinced that if you're looking for a body/brain improvement combo, dancing is your best bet? Check out the YouTube video *Mark Ballas on the Health Benefits of Dance*.[26]

Mark is one of the pros on *Dancing with the Stars*.

---

[25] Kivipelto, et.al. (2005). Obesity and vascular risk factors at midlife and the risk of dementia and Alzheimer['s] disease. Archives of Neurology (10), 1558-60.
[26] Watch the video at: http://youtu.be/LFaYV095zG0

Dancing Will Make You Happier

5

Looking for Happiness in All the Wrong Places

Our Constitution guarantees us the right to pursue happiness, but doesn't tell us precisely what happiness is or where to find it. Most wander from haystack to haystack, rummaging randomly for that maddeningly elusive needle.

Fortunately, theorists in the relatively new field of *Positive Psychology* have picked up where the Constitution left off. They've shed light on the nature of happiness and how we might acquire it. Positive Psychology focuses on people who are in good or exceptional emotional shape.

Happy Is as Happy Feels

Happiness is a state of subjective well-being. That means only *we* can judge the degree to which we are happy. A physician can tell you whether your arm is broken, but not whether you're happy.

Happiness is conceptualized as overall life-satisfaction combined with a propensity for having, on a day-to-day basis, more positive than negative experiences. Also, happiness seems to consist of three basic elements: *pleasure*, *engagement* and *meaning*.

Pleasure is defined as the feel-good aspect of happiness. Surprisingly, pleasure is considered the least necessary ingredient.

Engagement has to do with whole-heartedness – an intense connection to family, work, hobbies, etc.

Meaning is said to be present when we know our actions contribute to some larger good.

Happiness may be as important to our physical health as it is to our overall quality of life. Researchers at Harvard School of Public Health, found that people who were happy, optimistic and satisfied with life, had up to a 50% lower risk for a first heart attack or stroke.[27]

What social science has to say about what will boost our level of happiness might surprise you.

Unless you've chosen one of the several varieties of monastic life, you likely spend much of your time working, praying – and even playing the lottery – in hopes of one day acquiring enough money to procure the things you believe will make you happy: a lovely home, a *very* cool car, an occupation that commands respect, a killer bod, a gorgeous mate…you get the idea.

But think about it… the famous rockstar Kurt Cobain had all those things and he killed himself. Amy Winehouse, another famous celebrity, did the same thing, albeit accidentally.

Most people believe having more money will make them happier. This myth really struck home for me about 15 years ago during an exercise conducted at The Option Institute in Great Barrington, Massachusetts. I had signed up for Option's Cadillac, month-long adult development program for the purpose of recovering from divorce and prepping myself for life as a single after 30 years of marriage. (Lest you make any unwarranted inferences about my vintage, know that I was wed at the age of 12, subsequent to having been bartered to a band of Gypsies.)

During the exercise to which I refer, all 40 participants were asked to reveal their net worth…and then indicate how much more money it would take to make them feel secure and happy. The results, well, *some* of the results, astounded me.

I was not surprised when a work-exchange participant, who had declared his net worth to be fifteen hundred dollars, said that if he had ten thousand dollars, he'd be a happy man.

---

[27] Boyles, S. (2012). Do happy people have healthier hearts? Downloaded from http://www.webmd.com/heart-disease/news/20120418/happy-people-healthier-hearts

Nor was I surprised when people who reported being modestly well-off said more money would make them happier – after all, I was in that circumstance and I'd said the same thing. What astounded me was that people who were flat-out *rich* also thought having more money would bring them greater happiness.

A woman who estimated her personal fortune at six million dollars thought having eight mil would put her on the express-train to Nirvana for sure.

Research done on people's beliefs about what will make them happy or happi*er*, confirms the truth of the phenomenon I witnessed at Option. We tend to think having *more* – more money and more things – will somehow catapult us into the happiness zone.

But are we correct? Is it, for example, true that having more money will make us happier?

Would a Million Bucks Make You Happier?

Yes…and no. Positive psychologists, such as the University of Pennsylvania's Martin Seligman, report having more money makes people significantly happier only when it shifts them from poverty to the middle class.

After we get past having to worry about being homeless or where our next meal is coming from, additional dollars bring much less happiness. Think of it this way: while a stack of pancakes will give a starving person a heckuva rush, it won't do much for someone who has just eaten. So, unless you stole this book because you couldn't afford it, having more money – believe it or not – is unlikely to make you any happier. At least over the long run. And for the record, acquiring the other commonly desired things and circumstances, a lovely home, a cool car, etc., won't do it for you, either.

Dan Gilbert, a professor who has been featured in television commercials for various products related to financial security, has conducted research on happiness. Dan's findings, delivered with the signature wit and verve that got him on television, will surprise you.[28]

The basic, bare-bones equation for happiness:

A set of personal attributes (e.g., gratitude, optimism)
PLUS
Fulfilling work that plays to your strengths
PLUS
Close and satisfying relationships
PLUS
Leisure or other pursuits that provide learning and challenge
EQUALS
HAPPINESS!

Can money buy happiness? Yes, but probably not in the way you think.

---

[28] *Dan Gilbert: the surprising science of happiness.* http://youtu.be/4q1dgn_C0AU

If you want to get the biggest happiness bang for the buck, purchase *experiences* instead of tangible items. You will soon get used to that new sofa, but a new experience will always be, well… *new*. And, the possibility that it might turn out to be absolutely terrific will provide anticipatory excitement that is highly pleasurable. Moreover, you will have memories of the experience you can revisit.

Positive psychology research also suggests that having *frequent* enjoyable experiences nudges our level of overall happiness upward. If you have only a certain amount of money to spend on recreation, you would be wiser to arrange a series of weekend getaways as opposed to an annual cruise.

One of the things I most appreciate about dancing is that it gives me something to look forward to most days. (Alas, the studio is not open on Sundays and Christmas). There is always something going on, and, regardless of whether I'm there for a private lesson, a group lesson, a practice session, or a party, I almost always have a good time. On occasion, I have a WONDERFUL time – which is why each visit to the studio is preceded by another happiness-booster, *pleasurable anticipation.*

According to positive psychologist Sonya Lyubomirsky, author of *The How of Happiness*, there are a number of steps you can take to make yourself smile more often:

- ❖ Express gratitude
- ❖ Cultivate optimism
- ❖ Resist comparing yourself to other people
- ❖ Practice acts of kindness
- ❖ Learn to forgive
- ❖ Cultivate and nurture social relationships
- ❖ Increase flow experiences (stay tuned for more on that!)
- ❖ Savor life's joys
- ❖ Take care of your body
- ❖ Commit to something whole-heartedly

Taking literal steps – in a dance studio – will take care of the last five items on that list.

6

Happy Feet

There is no question that dancing makes people happier. I'm certainly happier now than I was before Arthur and I started going steady, and most of the folks I've interviewed for this book have said the same thing:

Mary Green, from Severna Park, Maryland, whom you met in Chapter 2, reports dancing made her happier:

Mary: I was not feeling fulfilled and I knew I needed something. I had traveled. I'd been to Mexico and Jamaica several times, but it was not rewarding. I'd spend the money and I'd come back and think, "That was a waste."

I needed something that would keep me overjoyed...and I'd say dancing does that. Dancing keeps me occupied and busy. Each year, I get a little better. I don't care how fast I move up the levels; I just want to dance and be happy.

Becca Hirsch, the satellite engineer from Maryland, agrees that dancing has added a bit of shine to her life, and that of her husband, John:

Becca: The degree to which dancing has enriched our lives has come as a complete surprise. When we were shopping around for dance studios, neither one of us could have even begun to envision the impact dance would have on us and the infusion of joy it would bring.

I had no idea how much I would come to love dance. I could not have imagined the effect it would have on our lives. It's changed our lives dramatically. It's just central to everything we do.

Mike Pasquerette is a military officer and instructor at the Army War College in Carlisle, Pennsylvania. Mike and his fiancée Pat McAvoy (they married subsequent to this interview), take group lessons from private instructor Frank Hancock, who teaches in their area. Pat and Mike are in agreement that dancing has made them happier.

Pat: *Happier? Yes.*

Mike: *Oh, yeah! I love it! I just enjoy it. I feel bad for people who can't dance. I see them at weddings and other functions, just sitting there and watching other people dance. They don't know what they're missing.*

Linda Weed, a schoolteacher who dances with various social groups in Maine, also reports being happier since she took up dancing:

Linda: *I'm a lot happier. The accomplishment of learning to dance and going to new places is just so satisfying. It's become rewarding on so many levels. It's definitely made me happier. It's provided me with a lot of high-energy and interest. It's something to look forward to doing...something else to think about and work on.*

Carline Coleman, who, you may recall, found that little muscle in her ankle, is happier because of her dancing, too:

Carline: *I'm definitely happier. I'm happier than I've ever been in my life. I feel as if dance has opened up a whole new world for me. And God willing, I plan to continue, because the more I get out of dance, the more I can give back to others.*

Kristin Daves-Croft is a middle-school teacher who dances at Arthur Murray York, Pennsylvania. Kristin started dancing around the time that I did, and has friendship in her life for the first time in many years:

Kristin: *Oh, I'm definitely happier; I've made one very good friend at the studio and there are a number of other people I enjoy being around. It's been 14 years since I've had a close friend. When I get up in the morning, I think about what I'm going to wear to dance class that evening. It's something I look forward to every day.*

Sharon Murry, a college professor in the field of Speech and Communication, has been dancing for over five years at a Fred Astaire studio in Greenville, South Carolina. Sharon has observed first hand dancing's amazing ability to boost happiness:

Sharon: *Over 50% of the students at my studio are single women aged 50+ and a lot of them are either recently divorced or widowed. Sometimes they come into the studio looking kind of beat up – worn out and tired.*

And very slowly, you watch them transform – just like butterflies. Six months to a year later, they're smiling, they're holding their head up higher, they're wearing sequins, and they're just happier. And I see that over and over and over again.

I've met so many people that I know would be helped by dance, and I just wish they would consider it. I hope you will emphasize in your book how much dancing changes peoples' lives...in ways they would never have imagined – the friendships you make, the connection with your teacher, the ways you push yourself physically, mentally and emotionally.

So what is it about what I think of as *dancin'* that presses the joy button in so many people? Well, making new friends and having to rise to successive learning challenges play a role for sure. After a lot of interviewing and a whole lot of reading, I've concluded there are a number of other factors involved as well: the physical movement and unique form of interpersonal connection inherent in dance, the powerful effect music has on our psyches, and the passion that I and many other dancers have for our favorite pastime.

Movement and Connection

Human beings have enjoyed moving to drumbeats and rhythmic sounds produced by other types of instruments for a long, long time. Physical postures that suggest the subject is dancing have been recorded in works of art dating back as far as 9,000 years. As you will see in Chapter 11, each dance, from Cha Cha to Waltz, involves a signature beat and distinctive motion. Dancers tend to have their favorites. Here's what Bonnie Stook, who lives in Annapolis, Maryland, and dances at the Severna Park Arthur Murray studio, has to say about how the movement and connection that comprise the very heart of social dancing make her feel:

Bonnie: *I think the actual physical movement helps connect with something very deep inside. For one thing, it fulfills the reason we have a physical body. It allows us to move so many muscles...and to move freely.*

Dancing is the closest thing I have found to flying without leaving the ground, because there are moves that just float across the floor...and it feels wonderful! That feeling of gliding is WONDERFUL! And you're doing it with another human being...and you're doing it in such a way that you are in sync, and it's just...magic.

I'm told a famous dancer once wrote that dancing is better than sex. What could he have meant by that? I think I know.

When dance partners are really in sync, whether because they dance often together or because they just happen to have terrific dance chemistry, it is possible for them to achieve a truly sublime level of connection and merging. For a time, they become as one – conjoined and lost in the movement, of which, paradoxically, they are no longer aware. In such moments, time seems to stop, the music goes unheard... and there is only rapture.

Becca Hirsch describes such a moment, experienced while dancing with her husband, John:

Becca: *When I dance with my husband, he communicates with me in a way that's so different from any other form of communication we have. I'm very verbal and John is not. So when we dance together, he communicates with me in a way that's powerful, yet gentle.*

And when we're really connected, it shows in our dancing; we can feel it and people who are watching us can see it – at least I think they can. It happened once while we were doing a Viennese Waltz at Showcase. Everything was perfect; we were both euphoric – we were in our own world. We could not hear the music or the people cheering us on. John said that was the most relaxed and the most competent he's ever felt while dancing.

Cindy and Bill Scullion are no strangers to dance euphoria, either:

Bill: *When you're moving across the floor and you're really hitting all the moves it can feel absolutely terrific. It's exquisite connectedness; you're in your own world – time stops.*

Cindy: *At Showcase, I did an Argentine Tango with Tim [T.H.], and couldn't have cared less what was going on around me. And it happened again during that event.*

Bill: *And the audience knew, because when that happens, everybody can see it. It's Wow! It's magic!*

Psychologist Mihaly Csikszentmahalyi has described such experiences in his book *Flow: The Psychology of Optimal Experience.* Flow is described as the mental state that occurs when a person is fully absorbed in an activity while performing it. It is a state of energized focus in the absence of negative emotions such as anxiety. The hallmark of flow, as we have seen, is a feeling of spontaneous joy or even rapture.

I've had some personal experiences with that magical state, although regrettably, not yet on the dance floor. I used to show horses when I was young. On one occasion, alone in the practice ring with my steed, I slipped into what I now know as Flow. All of a sudden, and for only a few moments, there was no separation between me and the horse. We moved as one, changing gaits and direction with seemingly no effort on my part. The signature bliss was there. That experience is as vivid for me today as it was nearly fifty years ago. While I never recaptured that state while riding, I hope to experience it again – on a polished floor, and with a different kind of partner with whom I am equally in sync.

Intimacy and Touch

Intimacy and touch are essential to happiness. Human beings are not solitary creatures. We evolved to live among others. As members of a social species, we have a biologically and emotionally-based need to establish close connections with others and to be physically touched by them. Of the five basic senses, only touch is essential for human survival. Infants deprived of emotional and physical closeness with a mother or other caregiver, fail to make expected gains in weight and height and have been known to die.

Healthy touch slows our heart rate and makes us feel safe and protected. Older adults have been shown to enjoy better health when they are free from what has been called *skin hunger* – the innate human need to be touched.

We are born with a need for connection and that need persists throughout life. When people are asked to estimate the degree to which various features and circumstances of their lives contribute to their happiness, an overwhelming majority ranks being close to other people even above even physical health.

The emotional connection to which I refer is known as *intimacy*. While the term often brings sexual connection to mind, intimacy can be present without a sexual component. As people in bad relationships know all too well, sexual behavior can be present without intimacy. The hallmarks of intimate relationships, romantic and otherwise, are empathy, understanding, compassion and trust. When we are intimate with someone, we feel accepted by that person and free to be who we really are. Moments of intimacy make us feel supported and safe. The anxious, lonely feelings that are ubiquitous in modern societies are alleviated, at least temporarily.

The reason intimacy in the context of a romantic relationship is particularly nourishing is that touch is involved. As mentioned, touch is something for which we have a built-in need. In this country, however, touch is mostly absent from intimate relationships that are not romantic. Our society is among the most touch-phobic on earth. In some other parts of the world, it is not unusual to see heterosexual male or female friends walking hand-in-hand or with their arms around one another. Here, unfortunately, such healthy and harmless behavior is cause for comment. You may recall President George Bush was widely castigated for having held the hand of visiting Saudi monarch King Abdulla, while walking with him.

A question subsequently posed by Ernest Gaines, Writer-in-Residence Emeritus at the University of Louisiana at Lafayette, may give you pause: "Why are we more comfortable seeing men holding guns than holding hands?"

Even American babies are touched less often than babies in other cultures.[29]

Our teachers are afraid to offer a reassuring hug to a child who needs one.

To date, 21% of American households are run by people who live alone. Plenty of us are in need of a venue in which we can enjoy close physical contact with other people safely and without fear of being judged.

Dancing provides us with the opportunity to be in touch-contact with others in a well-intentioned and mutually acceptable way. That kind of touch causes participants' levels of a hormone called *oxytocin* to rise. Oxytocin is known as the bonding hormone and its release is one of the factors that promotes a sense of connection among people who dance together.

---

[29] Heller, S. (1997). *The Vital Touch*. New York: Henry Holt & Company.

Other connection-promoting factors include a shared love of music, and common understanding of the joys – and difficulties – inherent in undertaking dance as a pastime.

These powerful forces of social connection soon weld strangers at a given dance studio or club into a community of dancers who empathize with each other's frustrations, celebrate each other's triumphs and provide caring and emotional support when necessary.

Kawoni Richardson, a quality-control specialist who dances at Arthur Murray York, Pennsylvania, finds friendship and community at her studio:

Kawoni: *My sense of belonging is very important to me. I wouldn't go there [to the studio] if I didn't feel involved with people there. It doesn't feel like a business – like you're just going there to acquire a skill. It doesn't feel like that. The friendships are the main reason I go there. I mean, dancing is fun, but it's become kind of secondary to hanging out with the people at the studio.*

John Grumbine, a 97-year-old retired businessman who was born in a log cabin, feels the same way about Arthur Murray York, Pennsylvania:

John: *The greatest thing, I feel, is the camaraderie. You're all there for the same purpose. The community is very important to me,* *because they understand what I'm doing; they encourage me. Getting encouragement from people motivates me to work to perform better.*

Cheryl and Don Youtz, whom you met in Chapter 2, have established friendships and participated in a wide variety of activities through their dancing:

Don: *We've done more travel than we'd ever done in our lives. The studio organizes trips to dance competitions and also pleasure trips. We've been to Tuscany; we've done a Mediterranean cruise; we did a Hawaiian cruise. We've met so many people who share our interests through dance – we go to their houses for Christmas. We travel with them. There are even organized swim parties at students' homes.*

We dance mainly in Leola, but we'll go to a studio party in Philly and stay overnight at the house of people we met on one of the cruises.

The dance community is 80% of our social life. If it went away, I don't know what we'd do. We belong to a group called Lancaster Cotillion Club and they hold six formal dinner dances a year and there is always a live band. The dances are held at different venues. Quite a few people from Top Hat belong.

We've also made friends we do business with – a painter, a dry-wall guy.

Earle David Reed is a successful stand-up comedian and radio personality who dances at Arthur Murray Lemoyne, with his inamorata, Tina Strausbaugh. Earle found a sense of community at his studio:

Earle: It brought me to a collection of people I never knew before. When you're young, you're like, 'Oh, I don't like that guy because he's a nerd or whatever.' But when you're older, you can look past that and appreciate people for who they are. At this stage of my life, I never thought I'd be meeting new people that were so interesting and so nice. I told Tina, 'This is great! These are really nice people.' And we have a common bond; it doesn't matter how long somebody's been dancing – there is a unity there. There's a brotherhood to it – a connection. I never had that before.

Pete Camasi, a retired county government employee, dances with his friend, Tish Dame, at Arthur Murray Lemoyne, Pennsylvania. Pete was both surprised and moved by the amount of support his dance community provided during his long recovery from a serious heart attack:

Pete: I never expected to get so many cards and letters. I'd get tears in my eyes reading them. I had no idea people from the studio cared so much about me – that I was so valued.

The Music

Music contributes to many people's happiness. It is a universal feature of human culture, and a very old one.

Scientists in the field of *Music Archaeology* (sound and sound-production in ancient cultures) believe prehistoric humans first began generating intentional sound, the beginning of what we now think of as music, between 35,000 to 45,000 years ago. They theorize that the first musical instrument was the human voice. The earliest rhythms are thought to have come from sounds produced while roots and seeds were being pounded into meal.

While most animals make sounds, only a few, such as birds and whales, create sound that can be considered musical. Humans, in contrast, are a highly musical species – and that characteristic develops early on.

While the young of most animals hear poorly or not at all prior to birth, human fetuses at only 36 weeks of gestation can hear voices and melodies…and remember them after they are born![30] This extraordinary affinity for sound patterns is thought to have persisted throughout human evolution because it conferred survival value.

While the young of many ground-dwelling animals are capable of fleeing from predators within a few hours of birth, newborn infants are completely helpless and must depend on their mothers for protection. A propensity for emitting a distress call when separated from Mom would have upped an infant's chances of surviving and passing on his or her genes. It has been theorized that sound-sensitive fetuses became accustomed to hearing the sounds of their mother's body (heartbeat, digestion, etc.), and as infants, shrieked in distress when separated from the source of those sounds.

Survival value may also explain music's persistence as a feature in human cultures. Richard Jordania believes the primary function of music in early human history was defense. A loud rhythmic singing that

---

[30] Gough, M. (2011). The origins of music. Downloaded from http://cosmosmagazine.com/features/the-origins-music/.

eventually developed into what is known as the *battle cry* was used, along with drumming and stone-throwing, to intimidate animal predators and hostile neighbors. Certainly it is true that even in more modern times, loud, rhythmic music was used to prepare soldiers for battle. Rhythmic repetitive music is known to be an excellent method of getting humans into a trance, or altered state of consciousness. The term *battle trance* is used to describe an altered state in which individuals about to go into battle forget their instinctive fear of death and may feel no pain during combat.

To be human is to be musical. Music has been a highly developed part of every known civilization to date. It plays an indispensable part in modern societies throughout the world. Music has a powerful effect on human emotions. It is used in visual and performance arts such as opera, musical theater, and motion pictures to induce audiences to feel appropriately sympathetic, loving, joyous, exultant, melancholy, sad, grief-stricken, shocked, or frightened. Music is also used in the advertising industry for the purpose of linking musically-induced positive emotions with specific products.

The reason music can affect our emotional state so profoundly is not completely understood. Various theories exist in the field of *evolutionary musicology*.[31]

One theory holds that music is an abstract form of human language. Like spoken language, it can convey a wide range of emotions, each with a signature pitch, tone, volume, etc.

Another theory holds that music reminds us of facial expressions that convey specific emotions in all cultures. A series of notes that descend, plateau, and then rise again, may evoke the same emotions that a smile would.

Still another theory is that music reminds us of various environmental sounds that soothed or stimulated our remote ancestors. Sounds made by a nurturing mother would have relaxed them. Sounds made by dangerous animals, however, and sounds of people running,

---

[31] Perlovsky, L. (2012). Cognitive function, origin, and evolution of musical emotions. Downloaded from http://www.webmedcentral.com/article_view/1494.

stomping in anger, or approaching in groups, would have put them on the alert.

Whatever the original reason or reasons, the emotion evoked by a specific piece of music is a function of multiple factors:

- the structure of the musical composition itself – tempo, volume and melody
- characteristics of the performing artist or artists (skilled, unskilled, enthusiastic, etc.)
- factors related to the listener such as personality, degree of musical knowledge and willingness to listen.

That music is personally important to individual humans is evidenced by the ubiquity of devices such as iPods, the popularity of concerts of various kinds, the efficacy of Music Therapy…and the fact that music is commonly played in the *boudoir*. Favorites in that locale, according to a survey conducted by Spotify, are the soundtrack from *Dirty Dancing*, Marvin Gaye's *Sexual Healing* and Ravel's *Bolero*.

There are a number of possible reasons why music is so important. One is that musical sounds (with some exceptions) are inherently relaxing. Silence is interpreted as a sign of danger by many social animals. Another may be that music is a wonderful source of distraction from troubling thoughts and worries. According to neurologist Oliver Sacks' wonderful book, *Musicophilia*, listening to music is an active process:

> *Listening involves a stream of inferences, hypotheses, expectations and anticipations….We can grasp a new piece, how it is constructed, where it is going, what will come next, with such accuracy that even after a few bars, we may be able to hum or sing along with it.*

That assertion rings true for me. Back in the days when I worked as a Registered Nurse in an Intensive Care Unit, music often played – at a low-volume – from a radio in the nurses' station. That was fine…until some emergent event caused me to need to think really clearly. When that happened, I had to turn the music off, because I found it so distracting. I never, however, needed to turn *talk* radio off, possibly because my brain didn't need to work as hard in order to process it.

I found Fox radio particularly undemanding.

Fair warning: if you take up dancing, you'll never hear music in quite the same way again. I've already confessed to occasionally Foxtrotting on woodland trails, unable to resist the siren call that emanates from my earbuds. Keith Heavrin, and his fianceé, Donna Freeman, who teach social dance in Bangor, Maine, are similarly enslaved:

Keith: *Everybody listens to music. It's on the radio. It's on everybody's iPod. But once you start dancing, it changes your relationship to music forever. You don't just hear it with your ears anymore; you hear it with your whole body. And once you hear it with your whole body – that changes your life. I mean, we've broken out dancing in K-Mart! And people have come up to us and said, 'Wow! Where'd you learn to do that?!'*

Linda Weed, the dancer from Maine, also has a hard time controlling her feet when she hears music:

Linda: *Dancing has changed the way I respond to music. I'll be sitting in the beauty parlor and I'll hear a tune and think, 'Oh, you could do West Coast [swing] to that.' Every time I listen to music now, I have a hard time standing still.*

The love of music, and dancing to music, is universal. If you doubt that (or even if you don't) access this grin-inducing video of a Moscow flash mob dancing to a distinctly American tune.[32]

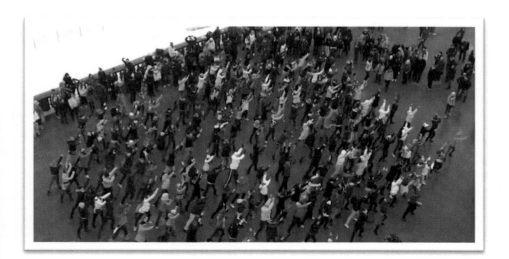

---

[32] Watch the Moscow flash mob video at: http://youtu.be/KgoapkOo4vg

The Bold

Quite a few interviewees said dancing enhanced their self-confidence and/or sense of accomplishment. Linda Weed gained self-assurance:

Linda: *I'm more confident. Knowing I have learned to dance…that I worked hard to accomplish something and have accomplished it…plus the fact that I'm putting myself out there socially, has really added to my confidence. When I first started venturing out on my own, I didn't know how to start a conversation or join one that was already going on, but I've learned, and now I'm much more comfortable.*

Dina Daubenberger relishes the sense of accomplishment she derives from meeting Ballroom's never-ending challenges. Dina is an accomplished dancer who's reached the silver-level in some dances and the coveted gold-level in others. A former commercial real estate attorney, Dina left her law practice a number of years ago to start a business, *Ballroom Dress Rental*, that reflected her passion for Ballroom and allowed her to remain at home with her two young children. Dina sees Ballroom as a way of constantly challenging herself:

Dina: Dancing with the Stars *was just getting started. And I thought to myself, "That looks so fun! I can see myself doing that." So I found a local studio that offered group lessons, and that's how it started. Dancing is a hobby I love. It's a definite 10 on the passion scale. It's something that is my own – that I can use to improve myself.*

I think sometimes people view dancing, particularly dancing in competitions, as, "Oh, I have to beat her," or, "I have to be at a certain level," but for me, it was never about that.

It's always been about how can I improve my own dancing? How can I get better? Because no matter how good you are, you can always get better; and that was fascinating to me – that you can do the same dance over and over and over again, and there will always be something you can do to improve it.

It's like golf in that you never get to the point where you say, "I've got it. I don't need to go any further." I love that about dancing; I love the inner challenge that it represents.

Dancing also allows adults to express parts of themselves with which they may have lost touch. T.H. and the other instructors receive their students as just that – students. While in the studio, we are free to abandon the demeanor and behaviors associated with the various roles we play in life. We can let our hair down, if we so desire, and be as goofy as we like. The bewigged clown on the left is the Harvey you've met before – a sober and responsible speech therapist – and the Goth chick on the right (pictured with instructor Luke Secar) is a certain college professor you've gotten to know fairly well by now.

Instructors put up with a wide range of ways of being and behavior (within limits, of course), thus freeing their students to be who we really are.

Good social dance studios are hot-houses in which the seeds of greater self-confidence and self-esteem are planted and then nurtured carefully. Studio protocols and practices mitigate, in so far as possible, the potentially ego-damaging risks inherent in attempting to master a new skill.

Most interviewees described their instructors as preternaturally patient – never ridiculing or reprimanding them. Interviewees said also that they get to practice their skills in an environment that is non-judgmental. Instructors are never heard comparing or disparaging students.

Studio patrons seem to pick up on the unwritten studio rules regarding civility quickly. During my first months at Arthur Murray, I noticed my fellow students never seemed to comment unfavorably on one another's dancing. I heard no snarky *sotto voce* remarks then, and have not to this day.

A research finding summed up by Sonja Lyubomirsky, author of *The How of Happiness*, may explain the connection between the enhanced happiness that dancing tends to induce and the benign atmosphere that prevails in most social dance settings:

> *We found that the happiest people take pleasure in other people's successes and show concern in the face of others' failures. A completely different portrait, however, has emerged of a typical unhappy person – namely, as someone who is deflated rather than delighted about his peer's failures and undoings.*

Studios also take care to preserve students' self-esteem in the evaluation process.

Levels and sub-levels of proficiency in partner dancing are designated by terminology (explained in Chapter 11) which varies according to the part of the world in which one is dancing. Students must demonstrate competence at one level in order to graduate into the next. Studios minimize the stress associated with performance evaluation by making it unlikely that anyone will "flunk the final" – students take performance tests (sometimes referred to as *checkouts*), only when their instructor feels they are ready. I, for example, graduated from bronze II into bronze III several months later than some of the other dancers in my cohort, simply because it had taken me longer (T.H. has the patience of a saint) to master all the steps and movements included in the bronze II curriculum.

Exhibition and competitive dancing, which is optional, is, of course, a bit more risky. While everyone is cheered and applauded, there is always the possibility of failing to perform as well as one had hoped.

I was very nervous at my first competition, danced poorly and was aghast when I saw the videos. Because T.H, the other teachers and my fellow students were so encouraging, I got back on that horse several months later, when the next event rolled around, and managed to acquit myself somewhat better. Not *well*, mind you, but better.

Sharon Murry (a.k.a. Ballroom Chick in the blogosphere) has accomplished something that is still on my bucket list: she has blossomed into a dancer who enjoys sharing her hard-won skills with an audience:

Sharon: *When I first came to the studio, I was very insecure, because this was a brand new world. I'd never danced before in my life. But my teacher was so gracious and kind...and he made me feel good. I started to gain confidence in several different ways, but particularly physically.*

I'd been afraid that people would be judging me for not looking good, or not looking like a dancer or for making a fool of myself. But what I found was the complete opposite. People were not nearly as judgmental as I'd thought they would be. I found that what people care about is the movement. There is a celebration of the movement...and I love that about dancing.

As I learned to dance, and learned more about it, I became more confident about dancing in front of people at the studio. Now, the nicest thing anyone can say to me is "I love to watch you dance," because that lets me know I'm bringing someone pleasure. Dancing is creating art. We all have art inside us. We all look for beauty. So if the audience is having fun, and they're enjoying what I'm doing, then I feel successful as a dancer. And that brings me a lot of pleasure.

I hope to someday achieve Sharon's level of confidence. I tend to be hard on myself as a dancer.

Dr. Peter Lovatt, a former professional dancer who earned a Ph.D. in psychology and now runs the Dance Psychology Lab at Herfordshire University in Great Britain, could likely have predicted that. Peter has identified gender and age-related patterns in what he calls *Dance Confidence* – individuals' appraisals of how well they dance.[33] During youth and middle age, women's dance confidence tends to be higher than men's. As women enter their fifties and men enter their sixties however, that pattern begins to reverse. Women's confidence starts declining and men's starts to increase, until older men's dance confidence finally surpasses older women's.

Do keep in mind, though, that while I may not feel as good about my dancing as I would like, there is no question in my mind that the humble pie I ingest regularly at the studio is a lot better for me than that other variety on which I used to fatten.

Peter Lovatt has also identified specific dance moves that women find attractive and unattractive when executed by men.[34]

---

[33] Lovatt, P. (2011). Dance confidence, age and gender. Downloaded from http://www.peterlovatt.com/Lovatt%202011.pdf

[34] Watch the hilarious YouTube video of CNN reporters viewing demonstrations of those moves here: http://youtu.be/X6bwbp7-2As

The Beautiful

If you sign up for dance lessons, you may well find yourself rooting around in your closet for something cool (or hot) to wear more often than you do now. Virtually all dance studios and clubs provide social events at which students can dress up, if they choose. Most host weekly or monthly parties and some offer special holiday and theme events which may be held in hotels and other such venues.

At competitive and showcase events in the ballroom world, discussed in detail in Chapter 14, old-fashioned elegance is *de rigueur*. Men wear black pants and shirts and women wear special dance *costumes* – long gowns or short dresses festooned with sparkling sequins, beading and crystals. Because what we wear both reflects and

affects how we interact with the world at large and how we feel about ourselves, there's more to getting snazzed up for a dance or a competition than you may think.

Lori Sweitzer, an OB-GYN physician pictured with her daughter, Isabella, dances at an Arthur Murray studio in Severna Park, Maryland. Lori is so fit that a friend of mine who saw her at an event commented that she looks like a "serious body-builder." Nonetheless, being a female in Western culture, Lori, too, had once been insecure about her looks:

Lori: *I feel more secure about my physical self – more confident; it's OK to get out there and dance and touch yourself on the hips, or touch your hair [arm-styling]...and feel good about it. If you had asked me five years ago whether I would wear that blue dress I wore at Showcase – the not-a-whole-lot-of-material dress – I would have said, "No way!"*

Bonnie Stook has also gained confidence – and sartorial daring as well:

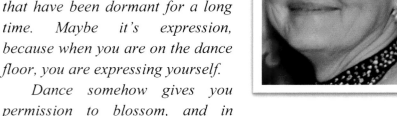

Bonnie: *I have more confidence. I have more social confidence, but I think it's more about being comfortable with myself. And I'm not sure how dance would give that to a person, but I think it makes it OK to bring out some of the things that have been dormant for a long time. Maybe it's expression, because when you are on the dance floor, you are expressing yourself.*

Dance somehow gives you permission to blossom, and in multiple ways. I would never, for example, have gone for these shoes [black and fawn-striped flats with a rosette]. I might have looked at them and chuckled, but never before would I have considered buying something that makes such a statement.

And makeup, too; I grew up with a mother who was not into clothes or makeup, particularly. I think that's just fine; it's nice not to have them be of great importance, but it's also nice to be comfortable with a certain amount of makeup.

I think our society takes a woman more seriously if she bothers to put a little bit of it on. So, something as simple as that made it safer to explore being more...female. And then there's the competition sparklies – the gowns, the bling and the glitz – it's kinda fun! And those eyelashes...it's like trying to attach a caterpillar to your upper eyelid.

Speaking of bling, remember Becca, the engineer?

Becca: *One aspect of my appearance that has changed has to do with dress and makeup. I wear more assertive makeup than I did, and clothes that have more flair and are maybe a little bit sexier. And bling – I never went for sparklies the way I do now...and I'm a satellite engineer, for God's sake!*

You won't have to perform at dance events in order to gain a new awareness of how you're presenting yourself. Plain social dancing did it for Linda Weed, the teacher from Maine:

Linda: Dancing has caused me to think more about how I'm presenting myself – about what my clothes say about me. I want to make sure I'm projecting an image that will be appealing to people I meet at dances. It's made me feel more attractive.

Male dancers appreciate the opportunity to spread their tail-feathers, also. Kevin Sand, a pharmacy technician who dances at Arthur Murray Central Pennsylvania, has fully embraced his inner Fred Astaire:

Kevin: I kinda sorta do feel more attractive. Especially when I get the suit on and the dance shoes…I'll get the swagger going – and it'll last even afterward, when I've changed into jeans and a tee-shirt. If I walk into a bar then, I'll feel like, you guys got nuthin' on me!

Amanda Spahr, a church secretary and A.M. Central Pennsylvania student, is significantly overweight (stay tuned for more about that from Amanda), but is beginning to accept her body:

Amanda: I struggle with self-hatred regarding my body. I really struggled with finding dance costumes [for ballroom events] that would fit. No one made one in my size. I finally found one made in China, and when I tried in on the first time, I just hated myself. People told me I looked nice in it, though, and I started looking at myself in a different way; I noticed that I have a pretty face and really nice legs. I'm gradually feeling better about my body, but I have a long way to go.

I really resonated with interviewees' stories of dancing causing them to feel more attractive...because I've undergone the same metamorphosis. In my sixth decade, I feel prettier *now* than at any other period of my life.

I'd always been a lopsidedly heady person – invested in and proud of my intellect, but neglectful and ashamed of my body. Dancing pretty much reintroduced me to said corpus, and to my continuing amazement, we've become pretty good friends – particularly now that I've lost a lot of weight. Flattered, apparently, that I've been paying it sufficient attention to have learned its ways and requirements, my body is showing an increasing willingness to extend itself...often literally... in order to comply with T.H.'s demands.

Hot for Dancin': Passion

Without passion man is a mere latent force and possibility, like the flint which awaits the shock of the iron before it can give forth its spark. ~Henry Frederic Amiel

As is the case with happiness, most of us know passion when we experience it, but might have a hard time coming up with a definition. A dictionary helped me out with that one. *PASSION: a strong or extravagant fondness, enthusiasm, or desire for anything.* That description captures perfectly how I, and so many others, feel about dancing. Amanda Spahr has been through more than her share of traumatic life experiences. Amanda spoke movingly about her passion for dance:

Amanda: I have a deep passion for it. Dancing brings me a profound sense of joy. The only place I'm 100% happy is on the dance floor. Dancing has definitely improved the quality of my life. Before I started dancing, I felt there was something missing. There was nothing I enjoyed doing. I would start things and not finish them. I tried sports, I tried crafts...and enjoyed nothing until I found dance. It's so hard to pin-point exactly what it is about dance that does it for me, but when I'm on the dance floor, especially when I dance a Waltz with Tim [T.H.], or something like that, I feel like I'm in heaven...like I'm on a cloud. There was this one time when I was dancing with Justin [Justin Howard] – this huge sense of joy came over me...and in my mind, I was dancing with Jesus...and that was during a really rough time in my life when I was feeling suicidal...and I just started tearing up with joy and Justin didn't catch on, and I was kinda glad he didn't, because I was able to have that personal time with God doing something I really love.

What drives passion? Why do people become passionately devoted to a given activity?

In a nutshell, passion is about doing something for its *intrinsic value* (I just love it!) rather than for secondary gain (I want to lose weight, please my wife, etc.). When we are engaged in an activity about which we are passionate, the effort involved, however great, never seems overwhelming. On the contrary – it is energizing. The poet David Whyte has written, "The antidote to exhaustion is whole-heartedness." How true! Because of my deep passion for dance, heading off as often as I do to spend various periods of time at the studio doesn't feel burdensome. It feels like the enormous privilege it is.

Bonnie Stook spends a good bit of time at her studio, too:

Bonnie: I dance as often as I can. There have been times when I've been there as often as five or six times a week. I have non-dancing friends who cannot believe how much time I spend at the studio. They'll say to me, "Are you going dancing again?"

We tend to find intrinsic value in – and be passionate about – ideas, values or pursuits that resonate strongly with who we really are. We all have an authentic self that lives behind the various masks we don in order to get through life. Our *true* self is not only unfulfilled by roles and tasks we undertake merely to get ahead, it is walled off and deadened by them.

Passion both emanates from, and nourishes, the soul. When we happen upon an endeavor that resonates with our deepest wishes and longings, our authentic self recognizes that which is soul-salvaging – and we fling ourselves into it passionately.

Miss Mary Green, the 76-year-old dancer from Maryland, is a tad enthused about dancing:

Mary: I love it! I think I'm addicted! It keeps me stress-free. Although I'm 76, it makes me feel like I'm 25. Dancing preserves us. Sometimes the money gets low, but I would eat oatmeal all the time if I had to, to keep on dancing. I owe it to myself. I'm going to keep dancing 'til the good Lord calls me home.

Psychologist Bob Schwarz posted the following question, and its implications, on the blog of the organization of which he is president: The Association for Comprehensive Energy Psychology:

Bob: What do you do that brings you joy or connects you with your best self? The bottom line is that we all need to do more of whatever that is. The pace of the world that we live in makes it very challenging to give the time and attention required to nurture ourselves and experience true pleasure, joy, connection, and creativity. Challenging? Yes. Impossible? No.

Getting Down With the Tribe:

The Studio as a

Therapeutic Environment

7

Lonely No Longer

Put Down the Weight of Your Aloneness. ~David Whyte

I've felt lonely.

Haven't you?

Loneliness is about feeling disconnected. It's about feeling isolated and unprotected on the front lines of life.

The painful emotion known as loneliness is thought to have emerged fairly early in human evolution. It's persisted because it had survival value – there is safety in numbers. Loneliness drove isolated individuals to seek the company of others.

Like our remote ancestors, modern humans feel insecure in the absence of connection with other people. We seek the comfort of connection in many forms. We enter into intimate relationships with romantic partners. We forge close relationships with family members and friends. We seek membership in various groups. For better or worse, we are besotted with social media such as Facebook.

While some of you may be thinking, *what I wouldn't give for a few precious moments* away *from my spouse, kids and co-workers* – taking a break is not the same as feeling alone on a leaky life raft with no horizon in sight. While it's true we tend to treasure occasional periods of solitude (and some can go for fairly long periods without other people around) no one welcomes the depressing and alarming pain of loneliness.

Unfortunately, according to John Cacioppo and William Patrick,[35] chronic loneliness is more common in our culture now than in the past, for a number of reasons. Families aren't as large as they once were. Many of us must work longer hours than our parents did, just to get by, leaving little time for socializing and membership in organizations and clubs. And then there's the Internet.

Whether the 'Net contributes to or ameliorates loneliness is controversial. Some studies have found that lonely people spend more time online than people who are *not* lonely, but in those, the issue of *why* is chicken-and-egg uncertain. Does spending too much time in cyberspace cause loneliness by cutting into time that could be spent in the actual company of other human critters? Or, do people who are already lonely navigate the 'Net for solace?

There's no clear-cut answer to that yet. A researcher who studied college students [36] found a correlation between Internet use and loneliness *only* among subjects who were online a mind-boggling 40-hours per week. And, it seems that *silver surfers*, elderly people who keep in touch with friends and family via e-mail, tend to be less lonely than their counterparts who don't.[37]

Nonetheless, psychologist Katriona Morrison says using online interaction as a *substitute*, instead of a *supplement*, for the real thing is a mistake. We need to be able to tune in to other people's vocal intonations, and read their body language, in order to really feel the connection we crave.

Loneliness Hurts and Harms

Loneliness is not only unpleasant, it's bad for our health.

---

[35] Loneliness: Human Nature and the Need for Social Connection, 2008.

[36] Katherine Dittman, 2003. Circle. Downloaded from http://circle.adventist.org/browse/resource.phtml?leaf=11106

[37] Cotton, SR, et al. (2014). Internet use and depression among retired older adults in the United States: a longitudinal analysis. The Journals of Gerontology – Series B. Published online March 26.

Loneliness, like hunger, is an uncomfortable warning that we are in a precarious state. Hunger can lead to starvation. Loneliness can set us up for heart disease.

Loneliness is known to confer a subtle and often vague feeling of *threat*. Feeling chronically threatened is stressful and can lead to unhealthy coping mechanisms. Lonely adults tend to consume more alcohol and unhealthy fats than their connected counterparts, and exercise less. Their sleep is less restorative; they report more problems with daytime fatigue.

Predicting who is at risk for chronic loneliness and stress is not as straightforward as you might think. The experiences that lead predictably to loneliness are not the same for everyone. Losing connection with a parent or sibling can be a more or less severe experience, depending on the relationship. Becoming divorced or widowed will be a lonelier experience for some than others. Not everyone is happily yoked.

Loneliness not only threatens physical health. It can also set up a vicious cycle that impairs emotional and psychological health.

Feeling lonely and threatened can prompt a tendency to be critical of others, which makes it more difficult to forge ties…which perpetuates the loneliness.

People who score high on loneliness scales also tend to experience more negative emotion – anger, anxiety and fear of negative evaluation – than people who aren't lonely. They also have poorer social skills and receive less support from other people.

Connecting

Dancing is a marvelous antidote to loneliness. If you join a dance community, you will up your chances of fulfilling your need for connection. You will feel like a member of a community, and you will make new friends. And – miracles *do* happen – you might even find a romantic partner…although I'm still waiting for that particular manifestation of cosmic prestidigitation.

As you become a regular at your studio or club, you will learn its customs, rituals and unwritten rules. You will become accustomed to the culture and begin to identify with it – *the* studio will become *your* studio. You will get to know teachers and other students and they will come to know you.

The ease with which you will make friends in a dance environment may surprise you. The common love of music and movement forges connection. Before long, people will start greeting you by name when you arrive – NORM! (Remember *Cheers?*)

Eventually, a most pleasant current of personal warmth will flow among you, the instructors, and many of your fellow students. You will realize you aren't lonely anymore.

Kristin: *I've definitely felt less lonely since I started dancing. After my divorce, I never went out. Now I have people in my life...supportive, fun people. Everyone is just so kind, and nice, and friendly. The studio and the people become your social life and you connect...there is something that binds us more than just the dancing. Differences don't matter, really. Like the age-range. There are people of all ages there, all ability levels, all shapes and sizes. Everybody's really nice. Not only nice...kind. It's a very positive atmosphere and you can really feel it. That atmosphere flows from the top, through all the instructors and right down to the students. I don't need to go out to clubs, even though now, I could dance in them. Arthur Murray provides the entire package – everything I need.*

Carline Coleman also leaves loneliness behind when she heads for her studio.

Carline: You don't feel lonely when you go to class. You have camaraderie with the other students. You get along. If the instructors see that you're down, they'll talk with you and it makes you feel better. And you can always talk to another student. They'll give you their phone number, or they'll call you. I'm not lonely anymore. I have a big family – four sisters and two brothers but I don't hear from them as much as I do from my dance friends.

Lori Sweitzer, the OB/GYN with the killer bod, has also been less lonely since she started dancing:

Lori: You meet new friends. So, yes, I would say I've been less lonely since I started dancing. You can go to the studio to take a private lesson, or a group class, you can go to practice and you can be around other people. And sometimes when you are feeling down and lonely, it's just nice to go there and be with other people who are happy to be there, too.

Reconnecting

Dancing can even strengthen the bonds between people who've been partnered for a long time. Instructors Keith Heavrin, T. H. (a.k.a Tim Hippert), Jameson Kilburn and Charles Sidman, a veteran teacher from Maine, have observed that phenomenon among their students:

Keith: The process of learning to dance together gives couples a connection point. After you've been married for a while, you can get sort of separate – and dancing brings couples back together. Once students learn the basics of connection, it changes their relationship. Now they can carry aspects of that joint effort into other things they do. We have been thanked, by couples, for showing them a different way of relating to each other.

Jameson: Early in my teaching career, I taught a couple who were not getting along. It was obvious to me they were trying dancing as a last ditch effort to salvage their deteriorating, empty nest marriage. The way they spoke to each other was not one that would benefit any relationship.

So as their teacher, I modeled for them different ways in which they could express concerns to one another and they responded to that. I also decided to make them physically walk a mile in
each other's shoes – I would sometimes have her lead and him follow – and that completely changed their respect for each other and everything about them as a couple. They ended up traveling with us, they competed

with us, and time seemed to go backward for them. They started to dress younger and look younger. They even started going out on weeknights, when before, they'd have gone to bed early. I really took that experience to heart and I've tried to apply what I learned from it to as many people as I can.

A coach once told me very few people go to a studio just to learn how to dance. He said, "Your first job is to find out what it is they're there for – what void they want to fill." I've learned many people are not consciously aware there is a void – many of us don't know what crosses we're carrying. And I think the process of personal growth – enlightenment, if you will – involves becoming aware of our crosses, and either putting them down or embracing them, and also doing what we can to help other people deal with theirs.

__Tim Hippert__: I've found that just being involved in the studio can really help a couple. Learning a skill together, the communication, the teamwork – having to figure out how to work together – all that's easier for some couples than for others. When two people are trying to learn to dance together, things are going to happen. Things aren't going to go right. Things aren't going to feel good at first – it's going to be frustrating. And how one person deals with that feeling affects the other person. If they can learn to understand their own feelings better and how to communicate them to their partner, that can be very positive.

Dancing calls for a whole new level of communication – we talk about one body, four legs. Two people trying to move in unison as one is not so easy, particularly at first. It's not like the guy is going to say to the lady, "Now I'm going to do this." It's communication without words. It's about feeling and connection and sometimes it's about looking each other in the eye.

A lot of people think that's silly when we tell them to do that, but really, for some couples, it's been a long time since they really looked at one another. I mean, two people who've been married for years and have kids and jobs – sometimes just looking into each other' eyes can be powerful...exotic for them...or erotic.

Charles: *A lot goes into teaching someone to dance. Teaching the figures from the syllabus is really the lesser part of it. The communication – the lead and follow – is a conversation between two people. Information is always being sent and received. I feel what is most important is the ability to create the feeling that there's no one else in the room besides the two dancers and the music.*

Earle David Reed, the stand-up comedian and radio personality you met earlier understands the difficulties inherent in learning to dance as part of a couple:

Earle: *It's hard to learn as a couple, because one person might need more attention than the other on a particular thing and it's hard to know who did what when things go wrong. When you're taking an individual lesson and dancing with an instructor and there's a mistake, 99% of the time, you made it! So we take private lessons individually and come together as a couple during the group lessons*

and the parties. We do take a couple's lesson occasionally, though. I think dancing's made me more patient; I've come to the realization that I don't know everything!

Dean Piskor, a pharmaceutical representative, and his wife Susan, take group lessons in Dillsburg, Pennsylvania, from instructor Frank Hancock. According to Dean, dancing inspired Susan to come up with a novel – and effective – way of managing their spats:

Dean: *My wife calls it "Invoking the Rule" – the rule being that we are not allowed to continue the argument. We have to practice dance steps for five minutes instead. It's the cheapest marriage counseling we could ever have.*

Once we get into the embrace and start to figure out the steps, we have to concentrate hard to remember them, and that clears our heads. It distracts us from whatever the argument was about. Because when you're dancing, you can't think about anything else. I mean, we tell people about invoking the rule as a joke, but it's not a joke. It really helps us. It's another way to make it [the marriage] work, and that's something we've had to work at for the last twenty years. We're very different people when it comes to arguing. I want it solved immediately and she wants more time. So, either of us can invoke the rule without taking anything away from the other person.

Katie Clark, who, with partner Shawn Groth, co-owns the Southern California independent studio The Connected Dancer (www.theconnecteddancer.com), has witnessed first-hand the magic dancing can work in a marriage.

Katie: I worked with a couple who had grown children who would be getting married soon. They came to the studio so they would be able to dance at those weddings. The lady was an artist and very expressive. Her husband was a lawyer and not as expressive. It was difficult for them to get in sync and dance well together. Both had strong personalities and neither was a go-with-the-flow person. They would quarrel over the lead and follow. The woman would ask questions like, "Do I always have to do what you want to do? How do I be a 'follow' and still express myself?"

It soon became clear those questions related not only to dancing, but their marriage, as well. Dancing requires both members of a couple to be fully present and engaged, physically and mentally. That intense connection sometimes prompts them to confront issues they'd been avoiding. It was so cool to see that couple work everything out, learn to dance well together, and be able to enjoy the process.

If you feel lonely – occasionally or most of the time – dancing can help. It can help whether you're single or in a relationship stale as toaster-tray crumbs. If the latter scenario hit home, I have the perfect book for you: *Ballroom Dancing is Not for Sissies: An R-Rated Guide to Partnership*. The authors, Elizabeth and Arthur Seagull, are both psychologists – and dancers. The Seagulls (love it!) guide couples through levels of relational expertise that mirror those used to indicate dance proficiency: beginner, bronze, silver, and gold. Their wise and witty advice is pretty much guaranteed to improve couples' partnerships – on and off the dance floor.

8

Jettison Your Jitters: Self-Doubt & Social Anxiety

Everyone who walks into a dance studio or club brings personal baggage. Some tote only a small valise, while others are wrestling with a huge steamer-trunk.

Performance and relational challenges spring the locks on dancers' luggage, forcing them to confront the contents. The good news is that while studios and communities are certainly microcosms of the larger society, most are kinder, gentler versions. People receive a generous measure of social support when old wounds reopen.

Still Crazy After All These Years

While my childhood was privileged in many ways, it was also somewhat difficult. I realized, during the psych-mental health portion of my undergraduate nursing education at Syracuse University, that I needed to work on myself – and I did. I read a lot of self-help books and attended workshops and retreats on personal growth and healing.

Over the years, I developed some insight into the dynamics of my early years and learned to cope with the resulting damage pretty well – most of the time. Nevertheless, wounds can be persistent critters and when I arrived on Arthur Murray's doorstep, I was still carrying a smallish overnight-bag's worth of insecurities.

As a result – and I find it absolutely mortifying to admit this – during my first year at the studio, I would feel rejected if an instructor or male student neglected to ask me to dance over the course of a studio party. I would review my inventory of flaws, seeking an explanation –

Is it my weight? My age? My looks? Maybe it's my lousy dancing. Even more difficult to disclose – because it's just SO stupid – is that the same feelings would arise during group lessons. Instructors typically demonstrate steps and patterns with several different students over the course of a lesson. If I were not among them, I would feel... *unchosen.*

Alas, logic is seldom allowed to intrude on neurotic self-disparagement.

An objective observer would note that it is easy for instructors to overlook someone, particularly at well-attended parties. They can do it unintentionally – I've suggested they be equipped with magic markers so they can initial our foreheads – or because the evening ended before they could get around to everyone. Said observer would also point out that during group lessons, instructors often demonstrate steps with whichever student is right in front of them – or with one unlikely to flub the step and be embarrassed.

A given gentleman might also have any number of reasons for inviting or not inviting a given lady to dance. He might prefer to dance mostly with his own partner – maybe she's the jealous kind – or he might prefer ladies in his own age-range...or a decade or two younger. Or, he might feel more comfortable with ladies at or near his own ability level. Moreover, many guys sit out quite a few dances – a fact of studio life ladies lament.

Happily, it is now rare for me to get that old rejected feeling at studio parties. But I'm still not immune to it when I venture off my home turf.

Occasionally, I attend club or public dances unescorted or in the company of another woman. Although I know groups of all kinds take a while to warm up to strangers, I still feel a twinge if I am asked to dance seldom, or not at all, over the course of an evening.

No wonder I'm so enamored of that Paul Simon song, "Still Crazy After All These Years."

Shyness and Social Anxiety

I'm lucky to have been spared two particularly challenging and common manifestations of emotional fragility: shyness, and its bigger, badder brother, *social phobia*. Shy people tend to shun the spotlight. They rarely speak up when among people they don't know well. Shy people suffer from a relatively mild degree of what is known as *social anxiety*. They fear the judgment of others. They fear being evaluated... and found wanting.

People who are extremely shy are said to suffer from *social phobia*, a.k.a. *social anxiety disorder*. You'll hear more about that shortly, when you are reacquainted with Kevin.

Being shy is not the same as being *introverted*.

Although both cause people to be perceived as quiet and slow to join in group activities, the difference lies in the reasons for their behavior.

Introverts simply prefer to think before they speak and look before they leap. Introversion is about *druthers*, not fear – and it is not a painful way of being. Shy people, in contrast, are gripped – to varying degrees – by *fear,* which is painful...and may have consequences. It is not uncommon for socially anxious people to foreclose their potential for achievement because they cannot bring themselves to risk failure or humiliation.

Shyness is thought to be about 40% genetic. If you are a bit on the shy side, you may have an ancestor to thank. Being quiet and diffident can be something of a handicap in Western culture, in which the *Extrovert Ideal* – valuing boldness, talkativeness, and self-promotion over more subdued characteristics – holds sway.[38]

In many people, shyness can often be lessened or overcome entirely. Being a college professor, I've seen many a quivering freshman graduate as a self-assured young adult. College campuses are excellent settings in which to ameliorate shyness...and so are dance studios. Both provide opportunities to meet new people and try fragile skills out in a safe place. Even more importantly, there are no dire consequences should something go awry.

---

[38] From Susan Kane's *Quiet: The power of introverts in a world that can't stop talking.*

Kristin Daves-Croft, the teacher who dances at Arthur Murray York, Pennsylvania, is no stranger to social anxiety:

Kristin: *I'd been in a bad marriage and it had been beaten into my head that I was not worthy of being cared about. I developed social anxiety and was afraid to go to the studio. But when I got there, I felt so welcome and cared about.*

Now I don't have anxiety attacks. I do still worry, though, that people are just being nice to me because they are nice people – not because they actually like me. I feel Arthur Murray is a very safe environment, though.

Miss Mary Green's shyness is a thing of the past:

Mary: *I was a shy person. I was raised back in the day and we hadn't been exposed to very much. We were raised to be young ladies. Even when I was 71, I still had a problem walking into places alone. I'd keep*

my head down. When I first walked into Arthur Murray, I couldn't even look at my instructor, Paul [Pietrzak]. And he said to me one day, "Why can't you look at me?" And I said, "I'm a shy person."

All of that's gone now. I couldn't even wear a sleeveless top, because we had been brought up to be covered. So now, I get to wear my little T-strap dresses and all of that. I'm a much more confident person now. The head is high, the shoulders are back, and I'm just fine. I just feel so good about myself. I don't even think 76.

Katie Clark, the dance teacher and studio owner you met recently, has witnessed first-hand dancing's amazing ability to help people expand themselves.

Katie: *I taught a gentleman who'd been through a very painful divorce. There were a lot of ups and downs during the lessons. He could be very emotional and we didn't always feel he was making progress. I was always trying to do a better job for him…to help him find whatever he was really looking for. He finally opened up and admitted he had difficulty talking to people. He wanted to be more social and outgoing, but he just couldn't. Other students used to say things like, "He's weird. There's something odd about him." Over the course of our working together for eight or nine months, he came out of his shell a lot. He told me he was starting to feel like he had something to offer. He became much more social and I started hearing comments like, "He's so much fun!" Dancing totally changed the way he interacted with the world. His perspective just shifted. And that was a wonderful thing to see.*

Healing

Remember Kevin, the pharmacy tech? Kevin used to be the poster boy for social phobia. You may want to grab a tissue before you read his story:

Kevin: I wanted to get out of my shell and meet new people and stop playing computer games all day; I think life should be lived, not played...but it was so hard for me to take that first step. I was scared. I'd tried to call the studio a few times but couldn't bring myself to do it. So finally, I decided to just drive over. But, I couldn't go in. I sat in my car for about an hour and a half going, 'Ok, I'm gonna get out...no, I'm not. I'm REALLY gonna get out now! No, I'm not.'

Finally, I did get out, and I walked up to the door, and I looked in...and I thought 'OK, I know what the place looks like...I can go home!' And I walked all the way back to my car, but then I thought, 'No, that would be a total waste of a trip.' So I DRAGGED myself up to the door again and walked in... and they were just getting ready to close. They said, 'We can help you tomorrow.' And I sank into a chair... and I think they realized that if they didn't get me then, they wouldn't. So this instructor, Randi, came over and said, 'Come on; I'll take care of you.' And she did. And she's been my instructor ever since. I owe her BIG. She gave me my life back.

The first couple of months were brutal. I mean, I was still in my shell and if one of the instructors or another student would ask me to dance, I'd be like, 'You want me to dance with you?? Get away from me, puh-leez!' It was to the point where a couple of times, I ran away...literally. I ran out of the studio. And Randi would follow me: 'No! No! Get back in here!' That was terrifying, but I'd go back in. Or, I'd be shut down at a studio party...practically in a fetal position in a chair...and she'd make me dance with her.

She made me feel cared about and I eventually got over my shyness. I felt nurtured to the point where I now consider Randi my little sister...my EVIL little sister!

The story of Kevin and his instructor, Randi, has a bittersweet ending. Randi eventually left Arthur Murray to pursue other opportunities. Before her departure, she gave Kevin a note that reads as follows:

Randi: *Kevin – You've come such a long way and I am entirely proud of you. It hasn't always been easy, but you have always risen to the occasion… and worked…and worked. Thank you. You have given my job purpose and not a lot of people get to feel that. Thank you for trusting me. Now keep kicking butt!*
  Sincerely, Randi

Randi would be gratified to know Kevin continues to blossom:

Kevin: *Thanks to Randi, and everybody, my social skills have grown, on a scale of one to ten, from like a negative ten to about a six at this point. Dancing has made me much more at ease around the opposite sex. Before, I would probably never have asked a pretty girl to dance. I would have said to myself, 'Oh, she's really cute.' And then I would have gone to the bar. Now it's 'Oh, she's really cute – let's go!'*
  My confidence level is steadily increasing now that about half my social life revolves around dance. Now, I organize dancing and non-dancing outings for people I met in the studio – murder mystery dinners, rock climbing, visits to comedy clubs – anything to get people out to have fun. Dance has made me so much happier, it's ridiculous. A year and a half ago, I would not have been talking to you like this. I'd have been sour and dour. I don't get depressed anymore, and if I do, it goes away quickly.

That Kevin placed himself in an environment in which he would not only be expected to learn a new skill but execute it in public – often with people he barely knows – is a credit to his fortitude and determination.

I was privileged personally to have witnessed Kevin's transformation and Randi's unswerving commitment. She, too, is a remarkable person. Perhaps our paths will cross again and I will find a way to demonstrate my admiration for her.

Dance communities can also help people recover from various kinds of trauma. Amanda, the dancer who spoke with me so movingly about her dissatisfaction with her body, suffers from Post-Traumatic Stress Disorder.

Amanda: Dancing has helped me get over my fear of men. I was raped at age 13 by a family friend, and later, at age 21 was in a two-year relationship that was physically, emotionally and sexually abusive. At one point, I was hit in the head with a baseball bat and was in a coma for 10 days. After that relationship ended, I finally met a good man who became my husband.

We wanted to take dance lessons to get ready for our wedding, but I was very fearful at the prospect of being touched by other men. I was able to voice that to our instructor, who was very supportive and approached me gently and carefully. At first, I would sometimes have PTSD flashbacks while dancing with instructors, but they were always supportive; they're so sweet. We kept up with dancing after the wedding and at first, when other men would ask me to dance, I would start to feel anxious and have to look around to try to keep my eyes on one of the instructors or on another woman.

At this point, I don't have flashbacks at the studio anymore, and I can dance with just about anybody. Counseling helped, too. I still have flashbacks in the car sometimes, or at work, but not when I'm in the studio. When I'm dancing, it's like my time with God; I don't know how else to explain it. Arthur Murray is the one place where I feel safe and protected. Dancing saved my life.

Dancing can even help military personnel recover from war-related psychological trauma.

JoAnn Tresco is a paralegal by profession. She was at the top of her game as the manager of a busy paralegal training center in Harrisburg, Pennsylvania, when her army reserve unit was deployed to Iraq. A year later, the JoAnn who returned to Harrisburg was but a bleak shadow of her former self.

JoAnn: *When I came home from war, my boss of five years who was a veteran, and a leader I deeply respected, looked at me and said, "What happened to the smart lady that used to run this place? Don't you remember anything?"*
Me: *Oh, my.*

JoAnn: *Trying to remember anything from my old life was like trudging through thick sand. Only one year had gone by, but it seemed like ten. I had known before I left for Iraq that no one returns from combat the same, but I had no idea how much of a mark that tour would leave on* *my soul. I had lost more than the memory of how to do my job. I had lost myself: my vitality, my innocence, my trust, and all of the zest I was known for. I couldn't rewind my brain. My heart and spirit were broken.*

Me: *Oh, JoAnn. That must have been awful.*

JoAnn: *I would hear, "You used to be the life of the party! What happened to you? Why don't you smile anymore?" My family was extremely concerned. My former girlfriends were afraid of me because when they looked into my eyes, they didn't recognize me. I couldn't go back to being the old JoAnn.*

Me: *So you became alienated from your friends and family?*

JoAnn: *Yes. No one knew what to say to me. Those that asked about the deployment found out they really didn't want to hear about it. My stories about stuff like the terror of running to a bunker as mortars rained down on the base upset them. Worse, as a JAG NCOIC (a non-commissioned officer-in-charge who works with military law) I was exposed to some horrible human behavior. Deployment can bring out the absolute worst in people. I saw and heard things that haunted me for years – things civilians don't ever hear about. So after a while, people stopped reaching out to me because being around who I had become was awkward. Everyone, including me, wanted the old JoAnn back, but she didn't exist anymore. She still doesn't.*

Me: *You must have had post-traumatic stress syndrome.*

JoAnn: *Absolutely. I couldn't sleep and, when I did, I woke up not knowing where I was. I still had the knife I used to take with me to the shower trailer in Iraq, and I kept it in my bathroom at home because I needed to have it there to feel safe. Any sound made me jump out of bed. Before Iraq, I was a vibrant, active woman who was never home. After Iraq I stayed inside my house.*

Iraq took a lot from me. My personality, my swag, my sparkle, my smile and my enthusiasm for anything. Anything. It took my femininity, too. I could no longer walk in heels. My feet had hard calluses on them and I had lost my toenails. I swung my arms like a man. I had aged 10 years or more.

Me: *What led you to dancing?*

JoAnn: *I remembered we used to dance Salsa in Iraq and that it made me forget the war and forget where I was. As long as I was immersed in the music, my heart was free. So I thought, if dancing could keep me sane in Iraq, maybe it could help me now. So I googled "ballroom dancing Harrisburg" and a listing for Pennsylvania Dancesport Ballroom came up on the screen. I called the number and booked a lesson.*

That phone call began a partnership with dance that has saved my life. It had to be divine intervention that the instructor assigned to me was Jonathan Kopatz, a former Airborne Ranger with the Army's finest, the 82nd Airborne Division. It had to be divine intervention for Jon to show up at a time when I needed someone who understood both me AND ballroom dancing.

Our work together was not easy. Jon challenged me to move with grace and elegance and to trust him blindly – to allow him to lead, and follow his lead, without hesitation. He challenged me to convey emotions with my face and body, including emotions like vulnerability that were very difficult for me. Early on, I would break out in a cold sweat, swear, pace, stomp my feet and throw things, but I pushed myself. And when I asked Jon to push me harder, he did. He understood the soldier in me. And, more importantly, he supported me. Over time, Jon and dancing enabled me to soften and learn how to feel again. Jon and dancing gave me back my joy. I truly believe it was not by chance nor by accident that I ended up partnering with Jonathan Kopatz. God did me a favor.

Wow. No wonder the signature line on JoAnn's e-mail reads, "Ordinary people can accomplish extraordinary things on the dance floor and in life...be extraordinary!"

Here's JoAnn and Jon gliding through a gorgeous Viennese Waltz at Pennsylvania Dancesport Ballroom in Hummelstown, Pennsylvania.

In showing up at their respective dance studios, Kristin Daves-Croft, Mary Green, Kevin Sand, Amanda Spahr and JoAnn Tresco each exhibited commendable personal bravery. To act bravely is not to be *without* fear, but rather to *proceed in spite of it.*

9

Stress: Fageddaboutit!

When you take up dancing, you will be amazed at its power to relieve stress. Whether you follow or lead, the music and movement will command your complete and total attention. When you show up at a studio, club or other dance venue, you will be distracted from previous ponderings almost immediately. Remember JoAnn and Salsa?

No Room for Worry

While you're dancing, you have no room in your brain for fretful cogitation. Your gray matter is busy processing the music, and dealing with whatever learning or performance challenges await you. Your overbearing boss and your mile-long to-do list will be crowded right out of your cranium.

When you take a lesson, you listen to your instructor, watch her or him demonstrate steps and patterns, and try to reproduce them on your own. I'm a *"follow,"* as opposed to a *"lead,"* so when I dance, all my attention is concentrated on my partner in order to perceive the subtle nuances of the lead. If my attention wanders, and I'm dancing with a relatively unskilled partner, I'm at risk for getting my tender tootsies trod upon.

Learning to follow has not been easy. "Leads" signal their intention to move in a certain direction, at a certain speed, via the connection (touch) points between them and the "follow." The reciprocal pressure leads feel in the connection points tells them whether the follow is responding appropriately – moving in the correct direction at the correct speed – within a tiny fraction of a second.

Follows commonly commit a number of sins…and I'm prone to all of 'em. They respond too late, causing the pair to go off-rhythm. They miss the lead entirely, or misinterpret it. Or, they commit the ultimate follow sin – anticipating the next step and executing it before the lead has initiated. Follows who do that are said to be *ahead* of the lead.

As a follow, I must react instantaneously to the lead's signal that we are going to change direction, or that I must execute a turn, or move in a certain way. I must also pay attention to the music's cadences. Some steps must be relatively quick and some slower. Some must be *held* (paused) for a second or so.

Sometimes – God help me – leads try to get me to spin.

Spins, particularly sequential ones, are a challenge. I've been prone to dizziness and motion sickness since childhood. My parents dreaded car trips…for good reason.

It was always a tossup who would barf first – me or the dog.

Ships and airplanes remain a problem, and I've learned the hard way I cannot tolerate carnival rides of any sort. On one infamous occasion (I think it was an outing to a state fair), I managed to upchuck from atop a Ferris wheel onto the unsuspecting crowd below.

While follows have to be on their toes – sometimes literally – leads have even more to do. They, too, must be highly attuned to their partners, and the music. But in addition, leads must *think ahead of their feet*. They must decide what steps to execute – in what direction and how fast – and be able to alter that plan instantaneously, should a collision with another couple seem imminent.

I'd hate to leave you with the impression that the follow's role is passive and relatively unimportant. According to Ballroom coach Maja Serve,[39] leads and follows have four equally important jobs. Leads determine the steps, the timing, the direction and the amount of power. Follows "listen" flexibly for cues, move their bodies as directed, "sell"

---

[39] Dance-Forums.com: Coaches' Corner

the steps (flash and pizazz), and collect themselves in between steps in order to await the next cue.

Distracted – In a Good Way

Dancing will definitely take your mind off your problems. The more time you spend on the floor, the less you will have available for anxious, stressful, rumination. Carline Coleman, who is the primary caregiver for her disabled adult son, sees her studio as a refuge from chronic stress:

Carline: *I was having difficulties with my mentally-challenged son. I just needed something, so I decided to try dancing. I enjoy it. I enjoy going there each and every day, when it's my scheduled time. When I start dancing, if I'm having a problem at home, Paul [Pietrzak] will start twirling me around and it just goes away. I call it twirling into forgetfulness. He'll ask me, "How was your day?" and I'll say, "Start twirling."*

Bonnie Stook appreciated the respite dancing once provided her:

Bonnie: *I took some lessons in order to prepare for a cruise – which turned out to have no dancing – but those lessons got me into the studio and I've never looked back.*

That all happened about a year after I'd brought my mother up to this area to live with me. She needed quite a bit of care. Although I didn't start dancing specifically in order to get a therapeutic benefit, I came to realize that dancing was a VERY therapeutic activity for me. It brought me exercise and socialization, and just good feelings all around, at a time when I really needed an outlet. And they gave out free hugs!

Lori Sweitzer, the obstetrician – a busy woman in a high-stakes career – appreciates having a place where she can relax her professional vigilance and allow herself to make mistakes:

Lori: *My dance community is almost like a larger extended family. It's nice to have a place where I can be more relaxed and can afford to make mistakes. I can try new things – new patterns, new moves – with little consequence. If I make a mistake, so what? I just do it again and again until I get it right. If I go to a competition and screw up, well, there's always the next time. It's a whole different thing in my practice. If I make a mistake, I could lose a baby.*

Earle David Reed finds, at his studio, respite from the demands of a very public career as a stand-up comedian and radio personality:

Earle: *The studio is an escape for me from everything else I do. There's really never any pressure on you. It's not like show business or someplace else where you're expected to put on airs or give off* *this certain vibe. People come from all different backgrounds, different classes, and we all can be ourselves and we all get along. Nobody ever asks me for an autograph or tries to get me to talk about show business. The teachers don't do that, either. So it's a real escape for me.*

Elizabeth Metzger is a social worker who now numbers Ballroom among the arts (voice, community theater and nature photography) in which she has become accomplished. Elizabeth is so enamored of dance that she makes the 140-mile round trip to her studio and back several times a week, spending an average of $500/month on gas:

__Elizabeth:__ I absolutely love dancing. I would rate it a 10 on the passion scale. It makes me feel good. It's great exercise and I've lost 30 pounds doing it. It also allows me to be creative and to perform, which I love to do. Dancing also helps me get through my work day. I have a very stressful job and dancing is something I can look forward to. The time I spend at the studio also gives me something pleasant to think about at night – something that crowds out the horror stories I hear all day at work. Overall, I'm definitely less lonely, and happier, than I was before I started dancing. I'm almost afraid to say this because I might jinx it – but I'll be in my car and I'll find myself giggling because I'm thinking of something funny that happened at the studio.

Dancing and dance communities can even help people cope with two of the most severe stressors we must all face eventually – grief and death.

Pat McEvoy, the financial planner from Carlisle, Pennsylvania, spoke movingly about how her dance friends helped her cope during her 25-year old son's lengthy terminal illness.

Pat: I could go dancing for an hour and just think about my feet. The rest of the world did not exist. There was just the music. I lived for that Tuesday night. After Kevin died, Frank [Hancock, her instructor] waited about two weeks and then he called and said it was time for me to come back to the studio...and I did...and everyone just enveloped me and it was so good for me. And I thought, "Oh my God, I love these people."

Mandy Kuhn, owner and teacher at Always Time for Dance, an independent studio in Lemoyne, Pennsylvania, also found solace among her dance community after a tragic loss.

Mandy: My husband, Chad Kuhn, was the love of my life. We met in college and just hit it off right away. Chad had been a wrestler, and had experienced a series of concussions. Today, coaches know concussions can be dangerous, but back then, they were not taken very seriously.

Chad found out differently. He had a lot of ongoing problems related to the concussions and even told me he thought he was only going to live to be 30 or 35 years old. As it turned out, he was right. We only had ten years together.

Early in our marriage, Chad asked me what I most wanted and I'd said, "My own dance studio." So he helped me make that happen. We were together every single

minute of every day up until he passed away from complications related to his brain injuries.

This studio represents his dream, my dream – the whole shebang. Dancing is the only reason I'm still alive. If I didn't have this studio and my dance friends, I would've gone with Chad. His death would've killed me. I know I'm young, but it would have killed me, because I only had two loves – Chad, and my work. Being able to go to the studio every day and having the support of my dance community is what got me through.

The support was really tremendous. There were about 250 people at the funeral and at least half of them were dancers. I had everybody sign a picture of Chad. It's hanging downstairs in the studio. Our students wouldn't have shown up if the studio hadn't meant a lot to them… if it hadn't changed their lives in some way.

This is going to sound weird, but Chad stayed with me for a long time after he passed. He helped me with most of the business decisions I've made. I'd ask him and he'd guide me about everything.

Dance communities can make all the difference to people who are themselves facing death.

JoAnn Tresco, the paralegal who almost left her soul behind in Iraq, told me a heart-breaking but uplifting story about Kelly, a young dancer who ultimately lost a long battle with breast cancer. Kelly's Dancesport community – and one very famous dancer she didn't even know – supported her all the way to the end of her journey. Here's a slightly shortened version of JoAnn's gorgeous memorial tribute to her friend.

EULOGY for KELLY SEBOLT ROGERS
PA Dancesport Ballroom, January 27, 2012

"For what is it to die, but to stand in the sun and melt into the wind? And when the Earth has claimed our limbs, then we shall truly dance."
Khalil Gibran

My name is JoAnn. Kelly Rogers was my friend for only about three years, yet I feel I've known her for a lifetime. There are some people who simply enrich your soul. I know Kelly meant a lot to many of you who could not find a way to speak today. I will be your voice.

I met Kelly in the dressing area at the back of this ballroom on June 26, 2010, during PA Dancesport's Summer Sundance Showcase. I had only been dancing about six months and all I had to offer at that time was a simple salsa. Kelly was in front of me in line and I'll never forget what she was wearing - a beautiful blue dance dress that, combined with her short red hair, made her look like a knockout. My contribution to the memorial table is that very blue dress.

Kelly danced a Night Club Two Step that evening. When she returned to the dressing room after a lot of applause, I said to her, 'That was beautiful, I wish I could dance like that.' She said, "You can." And then she flashed that Kelly smile, and even though she didn't know me, waited for me to finish my dance and clapped for me. Then she said, "I'm Kelly. Come sit with me." And she encouraged me to learn Night Club Two Step.

The friendship that began that night helped me to step outside of my comfort zone and try new things. The first lesson Kelly taught me is never stop yourself from trying something you want to do.

Kelly's favorite dance partner was undoubtedly her instructor, Jonathan Kopatz. Kelly was one of Jon's longest-standing students. They had begun dancing together in 2007 when Jon was a new instructor, so they grew up in dance together. Jon says Kelly was instrumental in challenging him to always stay a few steps ahead of her, which was significant in moving HIM forward in many dances.

Jon's favorite routine with Kelly was the disco number they performed during the 2011 Winter Exhibition. There is a framed photo of them in their costumes on the memorial table. Jon, I hope you know how much you meant to Kelly, and how much dancing with you added to the joy in her life. That photo of the two of you was her very favorite. Please take it home with you. Kelly would want you to have it.

We all know Kelly had a generous soul and was full of sparkle and life. She loved chatting with everyone. She would smile and laugh in a way that had everyone smiling and laughing along with her, no matter what they had going on in their lives.

Kelly was all about music. When she and I made the 10-hour one-way drive to my mother's condo in Myrtle Beach, she got into my car with literally one-hundred CDs. We put the convertible top down and sang, and car-seat-danced for hours on end. That was Kelly! The next lesson I learned from her was live life with MUSIC.

When I first met Kelly, I had just returned from a combat tour in Iraq and was in need of healing, so I took Kelly's lead and began to step out onto this ballroom floor, leaving behind what needed to be left. So the third lesson I learned from Kelly Rogers was that dance makes things better.

In 2012 Kelly learned the cancer she thought she'd defeated was back. By that time I had a small but close circle of dance friends – and we were all scared for Kelly. Because I'd had experience with fear of death as a soldier, and because I wanted to repay Kelly for the lessons she's taught to me, my friends and I vowed to remain with her and support her, even when the going got tough.

The going got tough quickly. One day, Kelly called to say her doctor had just told her she had six months to live – if she could tolerate a new and very strong type of chemotherapy. Kelly's response was to leave the oncologist's office and meet her sons at Hershey Park to ride roller coasters. When I texted her later that day to ask if she was okay, she texted back that she was dancing in the rain in front of the park's carousel.

No one defied death like Kelly Rogers did. In the months that followed, we watched her exhibit grace, dignity and courage in the face of severe reactions to the chemo and waning strength. The fourth lesson I learned from Kelly was grab life with both hands and live it, no matter what.

I didn't know what more to do for Kelly. None of us did. So we decided to ask her a question: If you could do one thing in the time you have left, what would it be? Without hesitation, she said, "Dance with Derek Hough from Dancing with the Stars. *" So we got on the internet and tried to get in touch with Derek.*

That's when I found out whatever I asked for in Kelly's name, happened.

I wrote an email to an unlabeled address at the bottom of Derek Hough's website. It turned out to be his publicist's. Within twenty-four hours we had a response...and tickets to the live premier of DWTS...and the promise of a meeting with Derek.

The angels were working overtime that day.

Despite obvious disease progression, Kelly traveled to Los Angeles, California, with me and another of her friends to meet Derek Hough. It was the trip of a lifetime. We not only met Derek, we met his family and friends and the entire cast. And Kelly's wish for a dance with Derek Hough came true.

Kelly's condition was starting to decline more quickly. When we returned to Pennsylvania in September and it was time to prepare for the December 1st Winter Exhibition here at Dancesport, we all started to pray that she would be well enough to dance in it.

Ominously, though, her condition seemed to worsen every week. By early November there were days when she couldn't get out of bed. Her doctors stopped the chemo and told her there was nothing more they could do. The cancer had spread to her bones and spine and she was on heavy pain medication. And yet, Kelly continued to dance. There were nights when I looked at her and wondered how she was moving, let alone dancing. That was another lesson for me: never stop the dance.

That lesson was best illustrated on November 26th when Kelly arrived here at the ballroom for dress rehearsal. She was scheduled to dance in two different routines – a solo with Jon and a girls' formation dedicated to her and breast cancer awareness. She had just gotten morphine at the pharmacy and she said to me, "It's bad, JoAnn. They put you on that in the end."

At first, I didn't think she would dance that night. She was in so much pain she asked Jon to wait a few minutes while she rested. Before long, though, I saw her get up and step onto the ballroom floor with Jon – and then I watched her nail her routine. She came back to our table with that Kelly smile on her face and said to me, "When I dance, I don't feel any pain."

Kelly's health declined further and soon she was unable to drive. The Rogers' house became "Kelly Central" as the kitchen counter filled on a nightly basis with wine and cheese. Kelly held court on the couch and eventually a hospital bed was moved in. Her golden-doodle, Marley, guarded her as we put up the Christmas tree and talked and talked and talked. Those were precious times. That was when the small circle of dancing friends met her family and her other friends and bonded with them. Every night when I drove home, I cried...but I also thanked God that we had had another day with her.

On Friday, December 14th, Kelly texted me and said, "I think I want to go to the dance tonight. I won't be able to dance, but I want to see everyone." I told her I would be her chauffeur. When I arrived at her house she was very weak and couldn't get dressed alone. So I helped *her dress and put on her shoes. I helped her into the car and we drove to the ballroom. When we got to Dancesport, I took her arm and led her up the ramp to the front door. She could barely walk. But as soon as she passed through the door she became the old Kelly, hugging everyone and smiling. It wasn't long before she was laughing as Jon led her out onto the floor to do a...you guessed it...Night Club Two Step. And then others asked her to dance. I don't know where the energy came from but she danced that night. The last dance of her life was a gentle Rumba with Jon in the corner of the ballroom, under the lights.*

On the way home Kelly talked openly and frankly to me about death. She knew it was near, and that the Rumba had been her last dance. I asked her if there was anything more we could do to support her. She said that instead of a memorial service, she wanted a dance. I remember saying, 'Kelly, how am I going to do that?' And she said with a wave of her hand and a giggle, "Oh just dance! That will make me very happy."

So, my friends, that is why we are here today.

Kelly, this is for you. Let's dance.

Give Your Bod a Break!

Your body will appreciate the respite from stress that dance provides as much as your soul. Stress, especially when it is chronic, takes a terrible physical toll.

The human body operates on what is known as the *fight or flight* principle. When it registers stress of any kind, it prepares for combat or escape. Early in our evolution, when our stressors were mainly *physical* – falling rocks or rising waters, animal predators or enemy tribes – that mechanism certainly saved our bacon. In modern times, though, our stressors are mainly *psychological* – negative emotions and anxiety-inducing thoughts – and fight or flight has turned into a killer.

Our bodies don't differentiate between physical stressors, which we usually *can* fight or flee, and emotional/psychological ones – which we cannot. The body responds the same way to an anxious thought as it would to a confrontation with a hostile and well-armed adversary. Our blood-sugar levels rise to provide fuel for battle. To minimize bleeding in the event of an injury, blood thickens and arteries constrict.

In the distant past when stress was mostly physical and episodic, these protective mechanisms saved lives. In the modern era, when stress is often psychological and chronic, they *threaten* lives.

Chronically high blood sugar levels cause premature aging of tissues. Chronically constricted arteries cause high blood pressure. Chronically thick blood may give rise to a clot that blocks off a coronary artery. That's a heart attack.

Chronic stress even shortens our *telomeres*. Telomeres are little "caps" – like those plastic protectors on the ends of shoelaces – which keep our gene-bearing chromosomes from "unraveling." Having your telomeres shorten to the point your genes deteriorate at an accelerated rate is something you want to avoid. That process leads to premature aging…and death.

For an accessible and informative overview of how factors such as stress, lifestyle and general outlook affect genes – and therefore physical and mental health – I recommend Dawson Church's book *The Genie in Your Genes*.

If I've managed to get you seriously stressed about stress, forgive me.

I had the best intentions.

I did it to maximally motivate you to mellow out…by taking up dancin'!

Everything

You Didn't Know

About Social Dance

10

"Equally a Sin for Both Sexes"

A Brief History of Partner Dancing in America

I was mesmerized by dancing as a child in the early '60s. My mother and father were accomplished social dancers. At some point, they even won a Jitterbug trophy – a gold-toned grail that occupied a place of honor over our fireplace. I wish I had managed to salvage that shiny symbol of the good parts of my early years.

My parents took me to dance-themed movies – *pictures* – as they were called then. Fred Astaire, Ginger Rogers, Gene Kelly, and Ann Miller were among the iconic hoofers who held me in thrall. I was fascinated by their gorgeous, graceful movements. I loved the clothes, the music and the romance. As an adult, I continued to seek out dance films of all kinds and became enamored of Patrick Swayze, John Travolta, and Mikhail Baryshnikov.

You may enjoy a terrific 6-minute video retrospective on the dancing that has enlivened American film from the 1940s to the present. The oldies are mixed in with more contemporary clips.[40]

What I didn't realize as a child was that earlier – much earlier – generations of dancers had paved the way for Astaire, Rogers, Kelly, and the rest.

Humans have incorporated movement into social interaction for thousands of years. Nine-thousand-year-old rock/cave paintings and carved figures suggest preliterate societies used dance to celebrate birth, mourn death, and, along with story-telling, transmit oral histories and mythologies from generation to generation.

The earliest evidence of dance in ancient European cultures comes from Homer's *The Iliad*. The classical Greek poet references *Terpsichore*, the goddess (or muse) of dance.[41]

Minuet, Anyone?

According to Judy Malnig's informative and witty book *Dancing Till Dawn*, today's partner dancing evolved from much more decorous and staid European forms popular during the 17th and 18th centuries. Dances such as Minuet, Quadrille, and Cotillion were formal and highly stylized. Up to a dozen couples, each standing side by side and joined only by their hands, traversed the ballroom in rows, forming intricate patterns known as *formations*. Male and female members (and would-be members) of the upper crust – there were climbers then, too! – used their skill in those dances as a badge of status and refinement.

Of course regular people – farmers, tradesmen and the like – were never allowed to darken a ballroom floor. They had to content themselves with a variety of *folk dances* such as jigs, hornpipes, and reels. Don't feel too sorry for them, though – the folk dances of the time were less formal, livelier, and likely a lot more fun.

---

[40] Watch the video at: http://youtu.be/9l5TrAXScbE
[41] Anonymous. The Project Gutenberg eBook of the Dance. http://www.gutenberg.org /files/17289/17289-h/17289-h.htm#c1

The contemporary equivalent of the folk dances of yore is known as *street dance*. Like their predecessors, today's street dances come into being where "regular" people gather – parks, the literal streets, schools, rave clubs and nightclubs – and reinvent themselves constantly. More about street dances in Chapter 11.

Abandoned Women Make the Best Dancers

Dancing has always had a habit of getting up in society's face.

By the 1800s, Waltz, and other closed-position, frontal embrace, dances began to emerge...only to be promptly condemned as vulgar and incompatible with ladies' fragile nature: *"There is something in the close approximation of persons, in the attitudes, and in the motion, which ill agrees with the delicacy of women...."*

The above quote is from an anonymous 1810 work[42] cited in Elizabeth Aldrich's scholarly yet hilarious book *From the Ballroom to Hell*. Aldrich's tome is titled after an eponymous chapter heading she found in an 1892 anti-Waltz tirade penned by the tightly-buttoned T.A. Faulkner. Faulkner's snit-in-print included other equally droll headings: *Abandoned Women Make the Best Dancers,* and *Equally a Sin for Both Sexes*.

Having sex on its side, Waltz eventually triumphed over its detractors:

> *We have now arrived at the culmination of modern society dancing, the dance which has for fifty years resisted every kind of attack, and is today the most popular known. From palace to hovel its fascination is supreme, and truly worthy of this universal love, for no other dance so fully gratifies the sense of rhythmical motion as the modern waltz with its poetic time and phrasing.*[43]

As Waltz – and her equally wanton sisters Foxtrot and Tango – were systematically seducing the general public during late 19th and

---

[42] The Mirror of the graces.
[43] Dodsworth Allen (1885). *Dancing and its relations to education and the social life.*

early 20th centuries, Cha Cha, Mambo and Rumba were loosening up its hips and knees. These and other wonderful dance forms from Africa, Latin America and the Caribbean quickly undulated their way into Americans' hearts – and into their dance halls and clubs.

Dance both mirrors and influences culture. The genres imported into the U.S. reflected the relatively more exuberant and less inhibited societies in which they originated. They influenced their adoptive culture by eroding, to a degree, the restrictions it previously placed on dancing and dancers. Nevertheless, immigrant street dances such as Tango and Cha Cha were not allowed to retain their original forms in their new home. They were toned down and "sanitized" in order to make them more acceptable to mainstream American sensibilities.

The Heyday of Dancin'

You may not realize that while partner dancing is quite popular today (thanks to *Dancing with the Stars* and similar shows), it was even more so in the past. According to *Dancing Till Dawn*, Ballroom was wildly popular from about 1910 through 1920, when audiences in vaudeville houses, cabarets and musical theater were being mesmerized by famous dance exhibition teams. Irene and Vern Castle, along with talented, but less well-known dancers, were discovering they could make a living through both performing and teaching their art.

Large New York City dance venues such as the Rainbow Room and Roseland, which could accommodate 2,000 dancers, drew huge crowds. Popular music, perfect for the various ballroom dance genres, was being penned by Broadway composers such as Cole Porter and George Gershwin. Few restaurants, nightclubs and community recreation centers were without a dance floor.

According to Libby Smigel[44] of the Dance Heritage Coalition in Washington, D.C., it was in the early 1920s that instruction in dance became widely available. Arthur Murray, who had studied with Vern and Irene Castle, inaugurated the Arthur Murray Mail-Order School of

---

[44] Arthur Murray (1895-1991) and Arthur Murray Dance Studios. http://www.danceheritage.org/treasures/murray_essay_smigel.pdf

Dance. Murray's system featured sets of numbered footprints that corresponded to the order and cadence of specific dance steps.

Hey, I could use a set of those! Wonder if any are still around?

Not long afterward, Murray established Arthur Murray, Inc., the very first dance studio franchise operation. Every year, my studio hosts a special dance party – cake and all – in honor of Arthur's April 12th birthday.

Dancing continued to be popular during the Second World War years of the 1940s. Jitterbug and other fast, fun dances, provided a much-needed escape from deprivation and stress. In the same time period, movie star and dance idol Fred Astaire established the second studio franchise business. I'll bet Fred's B-day gets celebrated, too.

Even as late as the 1960s, most small bars and restaurants had a jukebox and a space for dancing. I recall seeing my parents take to the floor in a number of such establishments, while awaiting the arrival of their entrees.

From Disco to DWTS

The Ballroom boom pretty much petered out in the post-war years, but dancin' – ever resilient – reinvented itself during the Disco craze of the 1970s. The term *Disco* (from the French *Discotheques*) was used to describe both the dominant street dance genre of the time and the dance-focused nightclubs it spawned.

The most iconic dance of the Disco genre was the Hustle – made famous by John Travolta in the film *Saturday Night Fever*. (I still can't believe there's only one Bee Gee left!) If the movie was before your time or you missed it somehow, check out John T. and his immortal moves.[45]

---

[45] Watch the *Saturday Night Fever* video clip at: http://youtu.be/LUID0jSh2Ic

During the Disco era, Hustle became the must-learn dance. It spread rapidly from the clubs into the studios and soon posed a serious threat to Ballroom. According to seasoned Arthur Murray franchisee, coach and judge, Rowland Dutcher, many studios scrapped Ballroom entirely during the Disco era, and taught Hustle only.

'SATURDAY NIGHT FEVER'

Nightclubs also offered lessons in Hustle – and some exciting and liberating new free-style dances as well. I'll bet some of you remember the *Frug, Jerk, Mashed Potato* and *Swim*, as I do. In those dances, couples moved independently, touching one another seldom, if at all. The popularity of Frug, et al., signaled a reversal in the trend toward increasing degrees of physical proximity between dance partners.

Disco, along with Funk, Hip-Hop and Electronic dancing – belong to a genre known as *Urban Dance*, which became extremely popular, particularly among young people who lived in cities. Punk music of the 1980s, and music videos of the 1990s (think Michael Jackson), continued a trend toward greater dance freedom and diversity right up to the present, when – for better or worse – dancing that involves not only close, but increasingly eroticized body contact has made a come-back. Dirty dancing (remember the Patrick Swayze –Jennifer Gray flick by that name?) is increasingly visible on television, in movies and in public venues.

Faulkner (the *Equally a Sin for Both Sexes* guy) would *not* approve.

Today, the social dance scene offers dance venues and styles to suit every taste. Ballroom-oriented studios and other organizations that emphasize International Standard, American Smooth, Latin and Rhythm dances are enjoying a resurgence of popularity. Clubs, teachers and competitions devoted to the "street" versions of dances taught in studios are attracting increasing numbers of dancers.

Nonetheless, most partner dance genres continue to mirror the sex-stereotyped roles that remain entrenched in society. It is still customary that in the case of mixed-gender couples, men lead and women follow. Happily, as contemporary women achieve in business, medicine, the law, and other fields that were once the exclusive province of men, they are beginning to demand equal opportunity on the dance floor. In West Coast Swing, and Hustle, for example, the follow role is becoming more active and interactional, particularly in the "street" versions of those dances. Leading on the part of women, and following on the part of men so inclined, is slowly becoming more common among heterosexual couples – most notably in the street dance cultures.

As the world turns, so does dancin'. The pace is slow, but that's OK – these days, I'm not moving that fast myself.

11

Hungry for Hip-Hop; Mad for Mambo —

Which Dances Will Turn *You* On?

Whether you'd feel more at home doing an elegant Waltz, a sizzling Latin Cha Cha, a funky Hip-Hop freestyle or an aw-shucks Country-Western Two Step, there is a studio-based or street dance community for you.

Ballroom

Ballroom, a.k.a. Ballroom Dance, is a studio-based genre christened after the formal, elegant dance parties of yore known as *balls* – remember Cinderella?

Contemporary Ballroom is divided into two main styles: International and American. The International style is older. It was developed by the British, mainly through two prestigious organizations: the Imperial Society of Teachers of Dance (ISTD) and the International Dance Teacher's Association (IDTA).

The American style is the new kid on the block. It was developed by the two major U.S. franchised dance studio chains, Arthur Murray and Fred Astaire, in an effort to kick traditional Ballroom up a notch while simultaneously making it easier for Americans to learn.

Should we feel dissed? I'm not sure.

Easy-peasy turned out to be popular. The American style is now preponderant in North and South America. International, however, continues to reign in the gluttons-for-punishment rest of the world. Both the International and American styles are divided into sub-categories.

Pay attention.

This is going to get a little complicated.

International-style ballroom is divided into the sub-categories *Ballroom* (a.k.a. *Standard*), and *Latin*. (I know that's confusing. Just go with it). The American-style dances are divided into the sub-categories *Smooth* and *Rhythm*.

According to the National Dance Council of America (NDCA), an organization that oversees dance competition in the U.S., the *official* dances in the International Ballroom category are Slow Waltz, Viennese Waltz, Slow Foxtrot, Tango and Quickstep. The dances in the American Smooth category are Waltz, Viennese Waltz, Foxtrot and Tango. These official dances are the ones highly-accomplished dancers perform in championship-level competition. The Ballroom genre also includes other dances commonly taught in studios and performed in lower-level competition.

Official Styles

International Ballroom / Standard	American Smooth
Slow Waltz	Waltz
Tango	Tango
Viennese Waltz	Viennese Waltz
Slow Foxtrot	Foxtrot
Quickstep	

The NDCA also allows Peabody, a perky, old-fashioned dance, to be included in the American Smooth category in sub-championship competition. There is no Peabody or Argentine Tango (another Tango from) in International Ballroom.

The dances included in the International Ballroom and American Smooth categories – Waltz, Viennese Waltz, Foxtrot and Tango – are fairly similar to one another, but there are differences in execution.

International Ballroom is a tad more uptight. Dancing couples are required to remain in what is known as *hold* – their face-to-face embrace. American Smooth, in contrast, is less missionary. At the lead's discretion, ladies can be positioned alongside or facing away from him, and can be turned and spun. There are also some differences regarding specific steps and patterns in the various dances.

The official International Latin category includes Cha Cha Cha (yep, three chas), Rumba, Samba, Paso Doble and Jive. The Latin dances are so-named because all have their roots in one or another of the Latin American countries – Brazil, Cuba, Argentina, etc.

The official dances in the American Rhythm category are East Coast Swing, Cha Cha (pretty much the same as the Cha Cha Cha) Rumba, Mambo and Bolero. The NDCA recognizes and sanctions sub-championship competition in other popular American Rhythm dances, which commonly include Hustle, West Coast Swing, Meringue, Bachata, Samba and Polka.

Official Styles

International Latin	American Rhythm
Cha Cha Cha	Cha Cha
Rumba	Rumba
Mambo	Mambo
Bolero	Bolero
Samba	Samba
Paso Doble	Swing
Jive	

While the International Latin and American Rhythm sub-categories have Rumba and Cha Cha in common, there is a significant difference in the way those dances are executed. In American Rhythm, most dances with roots in a Latin country must feature what is known as *Cuban motion* – a bending and straightening of the legs that generates a signature swiveling hip movement. In the International style, there is no Cuban motion. Legs remain more or less straight. Tight turns and quick swivels are emphasized.

More information on the International and American styles of Ballroom dance, as well as information about where the various dances actually came from, may be found in *The Complete Book of Ballroom Dancing* by Richard M. Stephenson and Joseph Jaccarino.

The word *smooth* is used to differentiate one set of American style dances from the other (*Rhythm*). Oddly, that adjective does not apply well to all the dances in the smooth category. While Waltz, Viennese Waltz, and Foxtrot do have a sort of smooth, gliding quality – Tango (a staccato dance), and Quickstep (which is a bit like running) – don't.

The factor that officially differentiates smooth from rhythm dances is the amount of progressive movement around the floor. Couples executing smooth dances cover a lot of ground – think of Fred and Ginger waltzing gracefully and rapidly from one end of a stage to the other. Rhythm dances, in contrast, involve minimal travel, particularly when done by social, as opposed to professional dancers. In Rumba, Cha Cha, Swing, Bolero and Mambo, couples remain in pretty much the same space throughout the dance.

Most Ballroom studios offer a mix of the official American and International-style dances, as well as many other popular dances: Hustle, Salsa, Merengue, Bachata, Argentine Tango, West-Coast Swing, Lindy Hop, Peabody, Polka and a sampling of Country-Western, & Line Dances. Urban (think Hip-Hop) dancing is making its way into studios as well. Some studios cater more to students interested solely in social dancing while others prepare dancers for the exciting, but exacting world of competition. Many, including studios in the franchised and free-standing categories, do both, according to the student's desires and aspirations.

So, what do some of the dances in the ballroom genre actually look like? Here's a visual introduction to the American Smooth and Rhythm dances to which you will likely be exposed if you begin your dance adventure in a Ballroom-oriented studio.

Waltz is a very old dance that, as you've read, has roots in Europe. The reason it is categorized as a smooth dance – its graceful, flowing motion – is obvious in this lovely clip of professional dancers covering a lot of ground in Viennese Waltz.[46]

Viennese is more whirly-twirly than regular, a.k.a. Slow Waltz. Social dancer Tracy Ludwig and her teacher Tim Hippert – T.H. himself – show you what your regular Waltz could look like if you work at it. I recorded them participating in an exhibition event, *Murray-Go-Rounds*, at my studio.[47]

---

[46] Watch the Viennese Waltz video at: http://youtu.be/WgSO_mouCaM
[47] Watch the Tracy and Tim Waltz video at: http://youtu.be/VXL06V_gJjs

Foxtrot is a smooth dance developed in America in the early 1900s. Originally a vigorous, jaunty dance done to ragtime music, Foxtrot matured, under British influence, into a flowing, showy dance that covers plenty of floor. Champion ballroom dancers Andrew and Lorraine Sinkinson show you how the pros do Foxtrot.[48]

Will *your* Foxtrot look like theirs? No, but hey, mine doesn't, either.

Here's another lovely – but more down to earth – Foxtrot illustrated for you by social dancers Glenda and Bill Hingley, who live in Victoria, British Columbia, and dance at the Victoria Ballroom Dance Society.[49]

Bill and Glenda also show you their Quickstep – a perky, energetic dance in the smooth category. Quickstep always makes me grin when I watch it.[50]

---

[48] Watch the Sinkinsons' Foxtrot video at: http://youtu.be/j9nOPUxjVrM
[49] Watch Bill and Glenda's Foxtrot video at: http://youtu.be/75xccT3aGxo
[50] Watch Bill and Glenda's Quickstep video at: http://youtu.be/_CGGyK7PZ_Y

On to Tango…the final smooth dance for which I've provided a video link. While most smooth dances are romantic or cheery in tone, Tango is in-your-face sexy. It's a dance of aggressive male advance and female *faux* retreat:

Him: *I want you!*

Her: *Mmmm. I'm undecided. Maybe you should try a little harder.*

Tango developed originally in Argentina – under circumstances mundane or lascivious, depending on which of the several tales of Tango provenance one wishes to embrace. My favorite holds that the dance arose in the bordellos of Argentina, during that country's colonial period. Impecunious gentlemen who could not afford an, *ahem*, full-service encounter with the lady of their choice settled instead for a sort of upright lap-dance that eventually became the Tango of today.

There are now three main Tango variants: International and American (the two styles of Ballroom Tango), and the original

Argentine variety, which itself has been subdivided into a number of regional styles. Becca Hirsch summed up nicely the differences between Ballroom and Argentine Tango:

Becca: *I love the passion and the staccato drama and precision – the emotion. Someone once told me that in Ballroom Tango, you dance with your husband. In Argentine Tango, you dance with someone who's not your husband.*

In the film *Shall We Dance?* Jennifer Lopez and Richard Gere convey the slinky, steamy essence of Argentine Tango.[51]

---

[51] Watch the J-Lo/Gere video clip at: http://youtu.be/HcGuq94enws

Tango done by folks who are not Hollywood actors is still dramatic – if a little less lascivious. Here's Cindy Scullion – all gussied up for Murray-Go-Rounds – and her teacher, T.H., executing an impressive Ballroom Tango.[52]

On to the American Rhythm category.

---

[52] Watch the Cindy/Tim Tango video at http://youtu.be/vqZTnASSMaY

Cha Cha has a flirty-cheeky, rather than torrid character. It arose in Cuba and was imported in the 1930s to England, where it is said to have been toned down considerably. From there, Cha Cha made its way to the United States in the 1950s. Here are professional dancers Karina Smirnof (look familiar, DWTS addicts?) and Slavik Kryklyvyy doing a sassy, sexy Cha Cha that doesn't seem at all toned down to me.[53]

Cha Cha done by social dancers is still plenty fun to watch. Here are Tracy Ludwig and Tim Hippert making Cuba proud.[54]

Rumba is another popular dance in the American Rhythm category. It is less flashy, slower and more sensual than Cha Cha. Dancing the Rumba puts me in touch with what remains of my inner siren. Said to

---

[53] Watch the Karina/Slavik Cha Cha video at: http://youtu.be/S_Oe07p8__Q?t=50s
[54] Watch the Tracy/Tim Cha Cha video at: http://youtu.be/voDTZlXF6p8

have originated in Cuba, and to have been influenced by the dancing done there by enslaved people from African countries, Rumba made its way to London in the 1930s, and eventually from there to the United States.

Check the footnoted link to view a stunning professional Rumba video.[55]

Remember: this is how the *pros* do Rumba. It's not how *I* do it and it's almost certainly not how *you'll* do it, unless you're reading this as a six year old, fall really hard for dance, and then commit the next ten years or so to a training schedule that would make an Olympic athlete look like a slacker.

---

[55] Watch the professional Rumba video at http://youtu.be/W2PNJRshJbU

Rumba done by regular folk who've been dancin' for a few years is still plenty cool – and hot! Here are Tracy Ludwig and Tim Hippert showing you how it's done. Bill and Cindy Scullion make a brief appearance, too.[56]

Swing is another extremely popular American Rhythm dance. When professional ballroom dancers compete in Swing, they perform what is known in common parlance as East Coast Swing. In ballroom studios, East Coast is often taught along with other types of Swing such as West Coast Swing, Balboa Swing and Lindy Hop.

Check out these awesome professional dancers tearing it up in a 2012 East Coast Swing pro competition final.[57]

---

[56] Watch the Tracy/Tim Rumba video at: http://youtu.be/2TqXLIPMrvk
[57] Watch the East Coast Swing video at: http://youtu.be/Yyt4Ff-NhPY

As you can see in the footnoted video below, social dancer Kawoni Richardson, whom you heard from in Chapter 6, has got the ballroom version of Lindy Hop down to a science.[58]

You may recall that some of the styles taught within Ballroom, most notably West Coast Swing, Hustle, Salsa, Country-Western and Argentine Tango, have parallel existences as popular street dances. Clubs/teachers devoted to a particular street dance genre may teach multiple versions of it. For example, a swing club might offer classes in East Coast Swing, Balboa Swing, West Coast Swing, Lindy Hop, Charleston, Carolina Shag, and others. Or, the club or teacher might be devoted exclusively to one version of Swing, such as Lindy Hop or West Coast. Dance clubs and teachers that focus on a single genre are usually tied into a larger network (community) of dancers with similar interests. In the interests of space, I'll introduce you to only a few of the thriving street dance communities available.

Swing

As mentioned in Chapter 10, Swing is a thoroughly American dance with many variants. There are two major street dance communities within Swing: Lindy Hop and West Coast Swing. I was fortunate to have an opportunity to learn about the large and thriving West Coast Community from respected teacher and judge, Kay Newhouse, who hails from Washington, D.C.

---

[58] Watch the Kawoni/Tim Lindy Hop video at: http://youtu.be/HWKYmEAeKXU

Me: *Kay, how did you get to where you are now in the West Coast Swing world?*

Kay*: I was a schoolteacher and I ended up working part time after school at an Arthur Murray because I wanted to learn dance and couldn't afford lessons. Also, I'm a teacher by nature. My co-workers used to take me out after work to the country bars to*

do West Coast Swing and Two-Step and I loved all that. Teaching dance was my fun job. I did that for about five years, which is longer than I had intended. It was a lot on top of being a brand-new schoolteacher, but I loved it. It was a stress release and a fun way to learn something and actually get paid a little bit for it.

Once I stopped teaching at Arthur Murray, I continued dancing. I did West Coast Swing almost exclusively, after a few years. Once I got to a certain level of skill I started getting asked to go places to teach. At that point, my youngest child was in kindergarten so that freed up some time. I've been home with my kids since my son was born ten years ago, so I've been teaching part-time. My teaching is primarily based on my love of the dance and wanting to build community and the dance. Those are two really important pieces for me.

Me. *Would you say that the East Coast community and the West Coast community are two different things?*

Kay*: They're pretty distinct communities. The primary swing communities are Lindy Hop and related vintage forms, and West Coast Swing. East Coast is a form that's not as popular nationally. It's an access form. It doesn't have the kind of national-level culture that Lindy Hop and West Coast Swing do. The most obvious difference when people are looking at those two dances is that Lindy is danced to more* traditional music – for the most part, an older sound – while West Coast is primarily danced to popular music. So if you walk into one room where people are doing West Coast and another room where people are doing Lindy, there's going to be a pretty dramatic difference and you're going to hear it immediately.

Me: I would call Ballroom a primarily studio-based dance culture but I'm getting the idea that Swing, particularly West Coast, is a very different kind of culture.

Kay: Well there is a dialect of West Coast that is taught in studios. It's made up of a collection of west coast figures, but actually, West Coast is a living thing that changes all the time. In fact, when people who have been inactive for a number of years come back into the dance, they really have a lot of new things to learn because it morphs constantly. It reflects whatever's happening in popular music and music videos. There's no actual West Coast syllabus, except what you find in studios.

The West Coast that is taught in most studios is generally not super-compatible with the style of West Coast that's really done within what's known as the 'Westie' community. Even in parts of the country where there are West Coast clubs and some studios teach it, it's still a very fluid community. Individuals are not generally attached to any particular club or studio or teacher, so they move around at will.

Me: So, if people want to know where to go to dance West Coast, or where there's going to be classes, or where to compete, how do they find out?

Kay: There's lots of Facebook presence. It tends to be geographic and people keep in touch with one another. In my area, Washington, we have a DC West Coast Facebook page that's kind of the centralizing piece for the area. It lists events run by area promoters. Also, friends will tell each other, "Hey – I'm going here," or "I'm going there." There is a network of people who keep in touch, and word gets around that way, too. Networks can cross geographically. For example, if I knew I was going to be traveling to, say, a town in Oklahoma, I could get on Facebook and ask if anyone has a contact in the West Coast scene there.

Somebody will get back to me and will be able to put me in touch with a dancer in that town, or an event organizer.

The World Swing Dance Council (WSDC) does have a registry that lists swing dance events, but that's very formalized, and there are a lot of Internet independent promoters who run events that would not be listed there; they would be publicized on Facebook and by word of mouth. I was into the West Coast scene before there was Facebook, and it was much harder to find dances and classes and whatnot then. In fact sometimes you would go to a venue on a Friday night and find the door locked. There would be no dance that night and it was harder to get the word out.

Me: *What are the levels of accomplishment/competition in West Coast? In American Ballroom, we have newcomer, bronze, silver, and gold, and some levels above those. Does West Coast have levels similar to those?*

Kay: *Yes. We have newcomer, novice, intermediate, advanced and all-star, although those levels do not encompass everyone since not everyone competes. And then, there's a separate category called champions, or invitational or professional, depending on who's running the comp.*

Me: *How does one get promoted from one level to the next? At my studio, you have to pass a performance test.*

Kay: *Advancement is not studio or club-based. It's competition-based and limited to accomplishment in Jack and Jill [described in Chapter 14] competitions. You get points for winning Jack and Jills, but not other kinds of events. The level at which you compete in a given comp is based on the number of points you've earned in previous ones. For example, you have to have a certain number of points in the novice category before you'll be allowed to enter a comp in the intermediate category. The WSDC keeps track of all that, at least for the comps under its auspices.*

Interestingly, we make no distinction between teachers and non-teachers. It's possible that a teacher who does not enter many comps, and therefore doesn't have many points, will wind up dancing against one of his or her own students, if that student does a lot of comps. People can petition to be allowed to dance at a higher level, though. And of course, there are phenomenal dancers who don't compete at all, and some extremely good social dancers who don't show well competitively. In both of those cases, their accrued points do not describe their level of dancing accurately.

Me*: If you want to be a West Coast teacher, do you have to get certified by an organization?*

Kay*: No. While there are some certification processes, the people who espouse them tend to be the people who've gone through them, and they are not widely followed or considered important.*

See Kay in action in the video noted below. Her oh-so-smooth dancing reminds me of sweet, hot syrup being poured onto something yummy![59]

Kay put me on to a Swing iteration that is both culturally and geographically specific – Hand Dancing. Hand Dancing arose in the African-American community in Washington, D.C. in the '30s and '40s and is still popular among older dancers, and, happily, increasing numbers of young dancers as well.

Markus Smith and Trendylon Veal, are professional swing dancers in the Washington, D.C. area. They describe their mission as "…promoting West Coast Swing and Hand Dancing nationally and internationally" (www.stuckonswing.com). Markus and Tren are true ambassadors of their genre, having traveled to France and the Ukraine and with pending trips to Spain, and perhaps Brazil.

---

[59] Watch Kay's West Coast Swing video at: http://youtu.be/zy4o0shWlM4

Me: I'm impressed by your international connections. How do you get to go to all those countries?

Markus: Through the Swing community. West Coast Swing has gotten really big now in a lot of different countries. Promoters from all over the world are beginning to come to the U.S. events and while they're here, they reach out to some of the pros who

stand out and are different and have something to teach their community back home. That's how it happens; we've never reached out to a swing community overseas; they get in touch with us.

Me: Markus, I know that in addition to West Coast Swing, you and Tren are known for something called Hand Dancing. I didn't know what that was, so I watched the documentary video on your website – and loved it. My parents were quite the jitterbugs, and the video reminded me of that. Is Hand Dancing still primarily a Washington phenomenon, or is it becoming more popular elsewhere?

Markus: I wouldn't say it's becoming more popular in other places. It's still a local dance. You wouldn't know about it unless you live in Washington, D.C., or Maryland. Every once in a while you might hear the term Hand Dancing in Pennsylvania or Virginia. There is a very interesting book on the history of Hand Dancing, Capitol City Swing, by Kim L. Frasier.

Me: Are there Hand Dancing competitions?

Markus: The National Hand Dance Association, which is something I'm part of, used to hold annual competitions, but for the last five years, Tri-State Connection has run them and they're going strong. Tri-State is an organization dedicated to promoting all types of swing dancing and passing it on to the next generation.

Me: *Did the lady who made the video found the National Hand Dance Association?*

Markus: *That's Miss Beverly Lindsay. She's president of the Hand Dance Association now, but she didn't found it. It was around before her time.*

Me: *Your website mentions you work with youth. Can you tell me more?*

Markus: *My work with young people began about two or three years after I began Hand Dancing. My instructor, Lawrence Bradford, wanted to bring in more young people so the dance would be passed down to future generations, but he needed someone who could relate to them. He invited me to teach the Saturday class, and under his tutelage, I was able to do that. This was at the Smooth and EZ Hand Dance Institute in D.C. [www.smoothez.com].*

Me: *Were the kids interested in it?*

Marcus: *No! The youth that came to the class were there because of their parents, not because they knew about it themselves and wanted to do it. To tell you the truth, I wasn't interested in it, at first, either. My mother had wanted me to dance for the longest time, but I was into sports and other things, and I didn't have dance on my mind at all. I didn't start dancing until I was eighteen – she got me to agree to try it one time. I didn't think I'd like it. I thought Hand Dance was really old school and not something that I'd want to be part of. In the '50s and '60s, kids did Hand Dance in schools, but today they don't. It's mainly an adult thing now, done in clubs. But my instructor allowed me to incorporate moves that were cool and fresh to me, and that's what allowed me to stay with it. If I had been forced to learn it only one way, I probably would not have stuck with it. So when I started teaching, I remembered that.*

Me: *So Hand Dancing was the cool thing for Washington-area kids to be doing back in the day?*

Markus: *Yes. In fact, in the '60s, there was a daily TV show called* Teenarama. *It was on WOOK-T.V. and it was basically a dance show – a forerunner of Soul Train – except the kids would Hand Dance to the music of the 50s and 60s. Sometimes they would bring in performers like*

James Brown and Marvin Gaye – different artists. You had to be well-dressed; gentlemen had to wear sport coats and ladies had to wear dresses. A lot of people don't know about Teenarama *because there is no footage left, but some adults today remember it well. It lasted seven years.*

Me: *Do you ever reach out to underprivileged or troubled youth and try to get them interested in Hand Dancing?*

Markus: *Yes. Under the National Hand Dance Association, we also teach in Ward 7 and Ward 8, areas in which a lot of the kids are underprivileged.*

Me: *And how do they react to Hand Dance?*

Markus: *Well, in the beginning, they don't know what it is, and they're pretty shy. It can look intimidating, depending on who they see dancing. They may think at first that it's not for them, but what I've noticed is that once we connect to the music they listen to, and we start to dance to that music, they are able to relate to the dance itself. Dancing has improved the lives of many of the kids we've taught. Their attitude changes, they become more comfortable just speaking to people. Their social skills get better.*

See the footnoted video for an out-of-this-world video of Markus and Tren Hand Dancing to, of all things, a Bachata beat.[60]

---

[60] Watch the Markus and Tren Hand Dancing video at: http://youtu.be/jsBrK4s7OFE

Now that you've seen the footwork involved in Hand Dancing, you may be asking yourself how it came to be called *Hand* Dancing. According to the website Who's Who in Hand Dancing[61] the dance is named for the crucial role the lead's hand movements play in successfully guiding the follow.

Hustle and Salsa

Like Swing, Hustle and Salsa are included in the Ballroom lexicon, and are also widely popular street dances with their own communities. I learned a bit about the Hustle and Salsa communities from Erica Smith, an accomplished and versatile dancer. Erica is a successful pro competitor, instructor, coach and judge in the West Coast Swing, Hustle and Salsa genres. Billed on her website as *The Hustling Attorney*, Erica[62] serves as assistant director of the Scholar's Program in Justice and Legal Thought at the University of Maryland, College Park.

Me: Erica, I'm curious as to whether the Salsa community is just about Salsa, or whether they do other Latin dances as well.

Erica: That varies geographically. I would say that in this area, if you go to a Salsa club, they're going to play a combination of Salsa and Bachata, and they're going to throw in some Meringue and some Cha Cha, although our Cha Cha is very different from Ballroom Cha Cha.

Me: Am I correct in assuming the Hustle and Salsa communities are similar to the West Coast Community

---

[61] www.whoswhoinhanddance.com/WHAT-IS-HAND-DANCE-.html
[62] To see Erica's outstanding moves, check the videos on her website www.thehustlingattorney.com

in that they're not studio or even club-based and that people communicate primarily via the Internet?

Erica: *Right on both counts.*

Me: *Do you have your own dance space for giving lessons?*

Erica: *I do. I have a studio in my home.*

Me: *Are group lessons offered prior to dance parties in the Hustle and Salsa communities as they are in Ballroom and Swing?*

Erica: *They sure are. The venue might be a club, a studio or even a hotel bar. And of course private lessons are available from teachers.*

Urban Dance

Urban Dance is an umbrella term that covers several major urban dance styles. While not a conventional partner dance form, Urban Dance is nevertheless a culturally important genre that benefits participants in much the same way as true partner dancing.

Urban Dancing was born in the '70s in urban America. Young people wanting to express themselves – but barred from mainstream dance venues – created their own movements in sync with their favorite music. Eventually, mastery of these new dances began to be demonstrated and tested via competitive exchange. Members of rival groups or "crews" would "battle" each other via a display of highly athletic and aggressive moves, either as a substitute for violence, or for community bragging rights. Over time, this battle-dance choreography spread beyond neighborhood exchanges and morphed into the urban dance forms that are tremendously popular today: House, Hip-Hop, Popping, Locking, Breaking, and others. While they retain their cultural authenticity in the underground dance scene, their community of enthusiasts is global and Internet based. Many urban dance styles are now taught in mainstream studios and clubs.

I asked LaTasha "Tasha" Barnes, an accomplished dancer and passionate Urban Dance advocate, to fill me in on her genre. Tasha is an instructor, judge and international competitor. She and her dance partner, Toyin Sogunro, won the 2011 Juste Debout World Street Dance

Championship in the house dance division and the 2011 and 2013 United States House Dance championships. Tasha serves as an Artistic Director for Urban Artistry (www.urbanartistry.org), an internationally recognized, non-profit urban arts project based in the Washington, D.C. area.

A woman of many interests, Tasha is also a fitness coach who operates her own mobile-wellness firm, Imani Wellness.[63] Impressed yet? There's more! Tasha also plays classical cello and piano.

Me: Tasha, what is meant by the term, urban dancing? What dance styles are included?

Tasha: Urban dance is a term we use to refer to all the dance styles that grew out of the urban experience, or were pioneered in urban settings. We use that term to include early styles like Lindy Hop, which has been popular since the 1920s, and the contemporary styles B-Boying, a.k.a. Break Dance, Hip Hop, Locking, Waacking, Popping, Jookin' – and my favorite, House Dance.

House Dancing is one of the styles I've specialized in. It's done to House Music, which is best described as a blending of Funk and Disco. Presently, there is some great Tribal, or Afro-House, music that inspires movement as well.

House is smooth, gorgeous to watch and – did you say you're looking for a workout? – highly athletic.[64]

Me: How about Hip-Hop?

Tasha: *Hip-Hop is one of the most well-known urban styles. It incorporates many other styles and influences – Vernacular Jazz, African Dancing, Popping, Memphis Jookin', Chicago and Detroit Jit, and New Jack Swing – to name a few. The beautiful thing about urban Hip-Hop dance is that it's so flexible. If you want to compete in all of those styles individually, you can do that, or, you can just blend them into your Hip Hop expression.*

Hip-Hop is a bit different from House, but just as energetic.[65]

Me: *Are there other major styles within Urban Dancing?*

Tasha: *Oh, yes. There's also Popping, Locking and Breaking, to name some of the best-known ones. The thing to remember, though, is that in Urban Dance, everything is interconnected. The styles may be separated in competition, but in social dancing, they intersect. They blend.*

To see demonstrations of these styles, check out the following footnoted videos: Popping,[66] Locking,[67] and Breaking.[68]

---

[65] Watch the Hip-Hop video at: http://youtu.be/4ctuYjmFNRg
[66] Watch the Popping video at: http://youtu.be/IsQAfL-PCX0
[67] Watch the Locking video at: http://youtu.be/YDPFgqIW-x8
[68] Watch the Breaking video at: http://youtu.be/QkcPFt77seM

Me: *Do you teach all those styles at Urban Artistry?*

Tasha: *We do.*

Me: *Can you tell me how you got into dancing?*

Tasha: *Sure! I've been dancing all my life – ever since I was a zygote, as my mother says. My dad was a D.J. and my mom used to go sit by the speakers when she was carrying me. She said that was the only time I would really move around in her womb! She tells me I came out dancing. Anyway, as soon as I was old enough, my mom put me in dance classes – jazz & ballet – and by age eight, I was dancing* en pointe, *which not a lot of girls my age in Richmond, Virginia, where I grew up, could do.*

My natural athleticism began to show around that age, too. My father was a football player in high school and my mother a track star, so I didn't have the long, svelte body of a ballet dancer – and realized I never would. So I switched to athletics and started with track and field, then competitive cheerleading. I eventually found my way into the military and got into serious power-lifting there. I started doing fitness competitions, too.

Me: *Tasha, when we first connected, you told me dancing saved your life. What did you mean by that?*

Tasha: *Well, in one of the fitness competitions, I injured myself very badly. I had to go through a recovery process that took a year and a half...and then, I was struck by a car.*

And that, of course, was not ideal – not at all. During the treatment process, the doctors diagnosed me with degenerative disc disease caused by the misalignment that persisted in my spine after the accident. They told me I might not ever be able to walk properly – and that even if I could, I'd have to forego athletics forever.

Me: *That must have been an awful blow.*

Tasha: *It was frustrating. But I wasn't going to just accept that I could never do the things I loved again. So I spent the next two years learning about corrective exercise, functional fitness, and different tools and modalities I could use to heal myself. I improved dramatically with the help of a rogue PT [Physical Therapist]. And I went farther than that. I got my certification as a personal trainer and corrective exercise specialist.*

As my education and therapy progressed, I came to realize Urban Dance might be able to help me regain hip mobility. So I signed up for a class in what I thought was Hip-Hop, but turned out to be Popping...and that turned out to be just what I needed, because Popping forces you to isolate and contract certain muscle groups at the same time you're relaxing others. Popping gave me a lot of confidence in what my body was able to do. In addition to feeling good again, I began to really enjoy the dance! One of the teachers, Rashaad Pearson, took notice and told me I'd probably be really good at House Dance. He introduced me to Junious Brickhouse – Urban Artistry's director and the floor captain for Assassins Crew, D.C. – when he was just starting to develop The House That Jack Built [see www.urbanartistry.org] and other Urban Artistry projects. The rest is history.

Me*: I've been reading up on Urban Dance, and I know it's very different from Ballroom and even other street genres. Are groups that compete as a unit always known as 'crews'?*

Tasha*: Sometimes. It's really a matter of preference. A crew can be a part of a larger company, or prefer to be known as a "company" itself.*

Me*: So, a crew is the same thing as a company?*

Tasha*: Yes...and no. "Crew" is a colloquial term for a group or team of dancers that work together and celebrate and value the same things. Most crews are united around a mission or ideal. They also compete and showcase their art. Dance companies are usually registered businesses that are for-profit – although some are non-profit. Companies can be performance-focused or education-focused, or both. Some are comprised of crew and non-crew members alike. To make it even more confusing, some professional, franchised organizations that are technically companies are also crews. Rock Steady Crew, for example, and The Universal Zulu Nation.*

Me: How would you categorize the teachers/performers at Urban Artistry?

Tasha: We are definitely a crew in the sense that we are a collective – a family. We all stand up for the same beliefs, the same mission. We want to make sure the roots of Urban Dancing are not obscured...that the cultural influences behind the dances that are so popular today are well-represented and understood...that they are not lost. But we are also a professional, non-profit dance organization focused on the education, performance and competitive aspects of urban cultures. So like I said, a crew and a company can be one in the same.

Me: When you say "cultural influences," do you mean urban African-American culture, or do you use the term more broadly?

Tasha: It's broader than that because urban dance culture itself is broader than that, but for the most part, it is about African-American culture. We want to make sure the unsung heroes behind today's popular dances are remembered and celebrated. For example, when somebody mentions Lindy Hop was borrowed from "other people," I'm going to be the one who stands up and names those other people. I'm going to say, "It was borrowed from African-Americans who created it from jazz-fusion in the 1920s, and it was also influenced by Irish-Americans and Latin-Americans.

Me: Good for you! I've been told that other forms of non-studio-based dance, West Coast Swing, for example, evolve very rapidly. Is that the case with Urban Dancing?

Tasha: Yes. One of the reasons it changes and grows so rapidly is that it encourages people to become more aware of their own cultural roots and traditions, and to incorporate that knowledge into their dancing. That exposes more people to different sub-sets of culture they didn't know about, and the process just grows. At Urban Artistry, we have a saying we borrowed from David Mancuso: [69] *"If you can dance together, you can live together."*

Me*: I love that! Tasha, do the Urban Dance styles each have their own communities? For example, is there a house community and a hip-hop community?*

Tasha*: Yes. The communities do identify themselves differently. They have somewhat distinct ways of dressing and moving on the dance floor, and of course dance to different kinds of music. But there are a lot of us who celebrate or dance more than one style, so we try to bridge the gaps or separation that some try to create to remind people these dances are meant to be shared!*

Me*: How do young people interested in this form of dancing learn it? Do they go to clubs or studios? Do they learn it from peers?*

Tasha*: Many dances are still created amongst peer groups and passed along the same way, but this is also the age of YouTube. All the competition and performance footage is uploaded immediately, and a lot of dancers – not just young people – watch them and try to emulate. Many popular Urban Dance styles are taught in clubs and studios now too.*

I'm proud to say a lot of young people within and outside the D.C. area come to Urban Artistry to learn. We've become synonymous with growth and empowerment. What my partner Toyin and I have been able to achieve in House Dancing, and the success of our mentor, Junious, and Assassins Crew, has brought a lot of attention to the D.C. area. We've had several international exchange students here, and that's a new trend. Most of them used to go to New York because many dancers see that as the hub of Urban Dance. But dancers – people – are

---

[69] In the late 1960s and early '70s, Mancuso, a New York City D.J. and social activist, held a series of underground, invitation-only parties that became known collectively as The Loft. Loft parties were unusual for that time period in that people of varied social status, ethnic background, gender, and dance styles listened and moved to music harmoniously. The Loft party concept became an international phenomenon and persists to this day.

learning that experiences and knowledge can be gained in a lot of different places.

Me: *I'm glad you brought the exchange students up. I've read that Urban Dance is now an international phenomenon. How popular is it among Caucasian people, Latin/Hispanic folks, Asians, etc.?*

Tasha: *Urban Dance – particularly House and B-Boying [a.k.a. Breaking] – are popular among many groups. Those styles are really big in France and Japan. People from those countries are very heavily involved in the competition scene. And some people have feelings about that. They feel our dancing is losing its soulfulness. But that tends to happen when something gets farther and farther away from its roots or inspirational source. I'm not suggesting people have to be struggling in life in order to perform urban dances well, but when you remove the historical context of the struggle that created the dances, the movement changes – you lose a little bit of the essence.*

Me: *Tasha, I'm wondering where women stand in these urban dance cultures. I know that in the west coast and hustle cultures, it's entirely appropriate for women to ask men to dance, and quite a few even learn to lead.*

Tasha: *Women are getting stronger in urban dance culture. We're rising up. We have a lot of creative influence that's being recognized and applauded openly. A lot of the time, though, we're still overcoming the stigma of the past – the idea that women are not capable of performing at higher levels, directing, teaching, leading organizations, etc. In my current experience, the main problem is women resigning themselves to support roles because they don't believe they can be or deserve more. But we are stepping out of the shadows and calling on our fellow artists to be responsible for the dances and cultures they celebrate. It's great seeing men in the community encourage and help to elevate more women, and also seeing women creating events and opportunities for themselves.*

Me: *Tasha, you've said Urban Dance saved your life in that it gave you back something that was extremely important to you – your strength and mobility. What other kinds of things does Urban Dancing do for people?*

Tasha: Well putting my trainer hat on for a minute, I'll say any type of movement, whether in the context of exercise or dancing, enhances our lives enormously. It helps us feel better – better physically, of course, and better about ourselves. That's because movement helps us maintain the suppleness of our body so we can fully express ourselves – whether through music, art or something else – and connect to the wider world. One of the reasons we continue to learn new styles in Urban Dance is that each style develops the body in a slightly different way, and opens us up to new ideas.

I also want to say Urban Dance allows people to acquire a deeper sense of who they are. People – particularly people with suburban lifestyles – often come to Urban Artistry with no understanding of what Hip-Hop Culture is or their place in it. It's enormously satisfying to watch them gain an appreciation of the rich culture that made them who they are...and its influence on Urban Dance.

Tasha and Toyin are just as awesome in action as you'd expect. Here's an example of the phenomenal footwork that made them world champs. In this video from a Juste Debout competition, Toyin, in orange, and Tasha, in pink and purple, compete against – and defeat – the *almost* equally fabulous FootworkKINGz.[70]

---

[70] Watch the competition video at: http://youtu.be/iQVp__Z1Fmo

The importance of urban dance to oppressed young people is captured in this quote from Gabriel 'Kwikstep" Dionisio of New York City: "When you grow up in the street you live to dance. After a while you dance to live."[71]

Country-Western

The Country-Western dance genre is very popular, particularly in Western states. Among the partner dances in this genre are Two Step, Three Step, Shuffle, Country Waltz, Country Cha Cha, and Country Swing.

Social dancers John and Kathy Hay, who dance at Arthur Murray Lancaster, Pennsylvania, have earned their spurs in Two Step.[72]

Ed Bollick and Karly Heck show you how easy, breezy Country Swing is done.[73]

Line Dances

In Line Dancing, one does not dance with a partner. People line up in rows and execute the steps individually. Line Dancing is a lot of fun, highly aerobic, and just as good for us as true partner dancing. Even social dance studios that focus mainly

[71] Saki Knafo. *Smooth Criminals: How Subway Dancing Became A New York City Art Form -- And A Crime.* http://www.huffingtonpost.com/2014/10/28/subway-dancers-new-york_n_6043552.html
[72] Watch the John/Kathy Two Step video at: http://youtu.be/wXD7pO_Qxa0
[73] Watch the Ed/Karly Country Swing video at: http://youtu.be/tp1pXdpfSac

on Ballroom may teach one or more line dances. At my studio, we occasionally do Hustle, Samba and Country-Western line dances at parties for extra fun.

Some years ago, Chris Dispenzieri of Bangor, Maine, bought a line dance lesson for herself as a 50th birthday present – and never looked back.

Chris: After I moved down here [to Maine], I decided I needed to do something. So I took up Line Dancing for exercise, because of course, it's great aerobic exercise. But in the back of my mind, I was thinking, "I could teach this." I could bring more people into it and also have a good time. Because of my musical background [Chris plays guitar], I caught on really fast and three years later, I was teaching Line Dance.

It started when a couple of people said, "Oh, you really know that dance, can you come give us a lesson?" So, I started in a friend's garage, and we had five people, and my fee was that they would bring me lunch. I would teach them some of the harder dances they'd been wanting to do. More people started to come, and so we moved to somebody's barn because we needed more room. And more and more started to come, and finally, somebody said, "You know, Chris, it's about time you opened up your own place." So I rented a dance floor. I had thirty people show up for the first class, and I was a little overwhelmed as I was a very inexperienced teacher. Now I'm up to three private classes a week and two at a senior center. About half of my original students are still with me.

I also teach a class for adults with disabilities. I have students referred to me from various agencies in town and the disabilities can be developmental or physical. I teach some blind people and some hearing-impaired people. And I have to remember who's who, because I have to be sure to stay turned toward the hearing-impaired students so they can read my lips. The class is really beneficial. For example, I have an autistic young man, and when he first came, he would just stand there and rock back and forth. But he eventually started gesturing to me that he wanted the music to start, and trying to do the steps, and now he laughs and grabs my hands, wanting me to dance with him. It was very rewarding, because when he first came, he would only stand and rock.

My oldest student is ninety-four and I have a couple of ninety-year-olds, too. They've been dancing almost twenty years. They can't move as well as they used to, but they can still learn and have a great time.

The big thing with Line Dancing is memory, so not only are you exercising your body, you're exercising your mind...and these people are keeping their minds sharp. It's a social organization, too. People keep track of each other. If someone isn't there for a couple of weeks, someone will call to make sure they're OK. And they will come in a half hour or so early and have coffee and socialize, catch up on each other's lives.

Watch high-energy Country Line Dancing via the footnoted link.[74]

There is nothing static about dance; it is a living thing that grows and changes constantly, influenced by the culture in which it is embedded. As cultures evolve, new dance forms emerge and old ones change. Dancers evolve, too. As soon as they master one level of accomplishment, they get invited – or pushed – to tackle the next. I keep waiting for T.H. to say, "Congratulations, Marian! You're done! You can take it easy now!"

Ain't gonna happen, though. One of the wonderful things about dance is there's always something new to learn. Always a reason to rise – again – to a new challenge.

---

[74] Watch the Line Dancing video at: http://youtu.be/_Qi3XgbD6-g

12

Shall We Dance? Absolutely! Where?

Unless you make your home in some really out of the way locale, say a tundra or a small island in the middle of the Pacific, chances are there is a studio, club or dance-oriented group in your area. You may also be able to find an independent instructor.

Studios

The term *studio* generally denotes a dedicated space in which dances within Ballroom, or other dance genres, are taught. Most studios have a smooth floor, usually made of wood, with full-length mirrors on most walls (wasted on vampires) and floor-side tables at which students can sit. Studios can focus on social dance, competitive dance or both. They can be franchised or independent, and can have one, several or many instructors.

There are two major ballroom studio franchise organizations: Arthur Murray International, and Fred Astaire Dance Studios, Inc. Both have hundreds of locations in the U.S. and abroad (no golden arches, though) and offer private and group lessons in a variety of dances. A third, Planet Ballroom, has recently established a foothold in the southern United States. The final chain of which I'm aware is Dance With Me. Founded by a consortium of *Dancing with the Stars* pros, Dance With Me has studios in a number of U.S. cities.

Franchised studios, and many independent ones, also provide students with opportunities to be coached by visiting luminaries. For example, I've had the privilege of being coached by Urs Geisenhainer, an internationally renowned dancer. Urs was a semi-finalist in the British Open at Blackpool, the most prestigious ballroom competition in the world, and reigned, for a time, as Arthur Murray Standard (explained in Ch. 14) Champion – talk about casting pearls before swine.

I've also been coached by Agnes Kazmierczak, one of Urs' former partners and a celebrated dancer in her own right. At the height of their fame, Urs and Agnes performed a dazzling Foxtrot routine as guest performers on *Dancing with the Stars.*[75]

Studios must meet the needs of two types of students: those who are brand new to dancing, and those who've been dancing for a while. Because the two groups have different needs, studios may have specialized staff to meet them. Katie Clark, who, you will recall, is a dance teacher and studio co-owner, told me how that works:

---

[75] Watch the Agnes and Urs video at: http://youtu.be/9sJCoocxBEg

Katie: *When I worked at Fred Astaire, I became the counselor – the teacher in charge of what is called the Front Department. The Front Department consists of new students and the teachers, called specialists, who instruct them. As the counselor, I placed new students with the right teacher and oversaw their progress. Sometimes it's the newer teachers who are assigned to the Front Department, but that's not always the case.*

We also had what was called a supervisor. That person was in charge of the Back Department. The Back Department deals with students who are past their first 20 or so lessons...students who are more advanced. Teachers who work in the back department sometimes, but not always, specialize in certain dances.

Clubs

While the clientele at studios are usually referred to as *students,* because they take dance lessons, clubs refer to their customers as *members.* Dance club members do not necessarily have to take lessons. They can avail themselves of only the club's social events if they wish. Members are usually charged a modest initial sign-up fee and may then attend social events and take instruction at a member discount. Unlike B.J.'s and Costco, most clubs make their services available to non-members also, but at a somewhat higher rate.

Teachers

Dance teachers are an eclectic group. They vary according to country of origin, where they ply their trade, how much general and dance-specific education they possess, and the skill level they have attained.

Oscar Restrepo is a Venezuelan-born dancer who has done well for himself in the U.S. Oscar and his former student Pam Bucher co-own BeyondDance in Mountville, Pennsylvania.

Me: *Oscar, I see by your webpage (www.beyonddance.com) you have a rich dance history. You've performed in Europe and the United States, taught for Arthur Murray and Fred Astaire, been coached by some famous dancers including Tony Devolani, and own your own studio. Do you compete, too?*

Oscar: *I do a little bit of pro-am with my students but I consider myself more of a show dancer. I like to create stories and then use movement and music to tell the story to an audience.*

Me: *Pam, do you compete?*

Pam: *Yes. I've done pro-am with Oscar in Arizona and Maryland, and here in Lancaster.*

Me: *Oscar, you were born in Venezuela. Did you learn to dance there?*

Oscar: *Oh, yes. I've been dancing as long as I can remember.*

Pam: *I think he was dancing in the womb!*

Oscar: My parents owned a traveling circus. I used to be a back-up dancer in the shows they put on. My father taught me to dance when I was very young.

Me: You mean your folks had a real circus with animals?

Oscar: No animals, but we had magicians and clowns and fortune tellers and there was always some kind of a dance show. When I got older, I performed Meringue and Salsa in large events that the government put on. That's why I think of myself primarily as a performance dancer.

Me: But eventually, you came to the United States.

Oscar: When I was 17 years old, I won a best dancer award at a big event in Venezuela. So I got a big head (laughs) and started traveling to other countries. I danced in shows in Spain and Italy and the Caribbean, and then, when I was around 21 years old, I came to the U.S. Eventually, I got hired to teach at the Arthur Murray studio in White Plains, New York, which is where I learned Ballroom. To this day, I am grateful to the manager, Michael Powers, for hiring me and for teaching me pretty much everything I know about the dance business.

Me: How long did you stay at Arthur Murray?

Oscar: Several years. I left there after I had met a couple from the Ukraine who owned a Fred Astaire franchise in Tarrytown, where I lived. Olga and Sasha Baylim were the most magnificent dancers I'd ever seen. To look at them doing Waltz was to see magic happening on the floor. I wanted to learn from them so I started working at their studio. Sasha helped me develop my dancing more.

Me: How did you become a studio owner?

Oscar: That happened after I decided to try professional competition. I was looking for a female partner and met Rebecca Gentry, who lives in Lancaster, Pennsylvania. She brought me to her home town so we could train together. We needed a space, though, and income, so we started Moonlight Ballroom. We thought we'd have just enough students to pay for our competing, but it didn't turn out that way. Before long, we were so busy teaching, we had no time to practice. We did a lot of pro-am, *and shows, but we never made it to pro competition. Eventually, Becca wanted to grow more, so she opened her own school, City Ballroom. I kept this one and renamed it BeyondDancing.*

Me*: Pam, how did you and Oscar get together?*

Pam*: My husband works for a hospital as a fundraiser. One of his donors knew I loved music and theater – I've been in shows at the Fulton – and introduced me to Oscar. Oscar still had Moonlight Ballroom at the time and he offered me three free lessons.*

Me: *He set the hook! I'm familiar with that strategy.*

Pam*: (Laughs!). Yep! At first, I took one lesson a week, but eventually wanted to learn faster, so I started taking two or three. I was a student at Moonlight for about two years.*

Oscar*: And then, when Becca started her own studio, I needed someone to take care of the other side of the business – the bookings and so forth – and Pam stepped up to the plate. She's been my business partner for about two years.*

Oscar went on to confirm something I'd suspected – that many dance teachers understand the transformative power of dance because they have experienced it themselves.

Me*: Oscar, when I told you about my book, you said, "Dancing changed my life, too." In what ways did dancing change your life?*

Oscar*: When I was young, I had a hard time in school because I moved to a new school every year. Some of the other kids' parents were doctors and lawyers and mine were magicians and clowns. I was an awkward, skinny kid, and very introverted. So to be able to go up to someone and ask them to dance and have them say "yes" was amazing for me. Because of my dancing, I became someone. I found out I could touch other people – physically and emotionally – and have them accept me. Every time I danced, I heard, "Wow! You're so good! You can really shake it!" That gave me such confidence.*

Me: *Oscar, you've had a long and varied career in dance. What is the most satisfying aspect of what you are doing right now?*

Oscar: Probably the most satisfying part of what we do now is our work with people in nursing homes. Pam and I, and some of our students, work with several different homes in our area – Willow Valley, St. Anne's – at least five of them. We go to those homes and put on little shows for the residents – dancing and singing – and we involve them with the shows, and we dance with them, too. Sometimes they come here to the studio in vans. We have had some wonderfully fulfilling moments with those people.

I remember a lady from Brereton Manor who was about 85 years old or so. She was bent and fragile-looking and when I asked her to dance, she said she didn't want to. But just then, a song called "Let Somebody Love You" came on. I think it was Michael Bublé or Frank Sinatra. So I got down on one knee, looked in that lady's eyes, and started singing, 'Let somebody love you.' And she stared at me for a second, and finally said – in an irritated way, "Oh, all right!" She took her sweater off, pushed her walker aside...and we started dancing. And soon, she was moving and loving it more and more. It was really great. It was wonderful.

Pam: They usually start off hesitantly and slowly, but once they get warmed up, you would be amazed at the movement these older people have. With the ones who cannot get out of their wheelchairs, we do chair dancing. They move their feet and their arms.

Oscar: There is another lady I want to tell you about. She said something to me that was very beautiful. We had just danced a Tango, and she looked up at me and squeezed my hand. She kissed my cheek and said, "I will never forget this dance. I will remember it in the afterlife."

Me: That is just gorgeous, Oscar. I imagine when you go to the homes, there are a lot more ladies present than men. Women tend to outlive men.

Oscar: Oh, yes. But even when I go out dancing socially and the crowd is much younger, there are still more women than men. If men knew the great secret of dancing – that women LOVE men who can dance – more of them would be doing it. In Venezuela, women do not outnumber men at dances. Men are encouraged to dance from a very early age, particularly if they are shy. All the cool guys are dancers. Girls know that guys who dance know how to relate to a woman. They know how to hold her, how to talk to her, how to make her feel safe and secure on the dance floor. They learn etiquette and manners, too. In fact, we are soon going to start a teen dance program here at the studio. Teens really need that.

Me: *That's fantastic, Oscar! I'm curious about why you named your studio Beyond Dancing.*

Oscar: *The answer to that question has a lot of levels to it. The obvious one is that some people come here to take their dancing to a higher level. They want to go beyond where they are now. But there's more to it. A student once told me her experience was beyond what she expected. That she'd done more than just learn to dance. She'd overcome some limitations, too.*

Certainly in my case, everything I've learned in life I learned through dancing. It teaches you how to communicate with somebody else, verbally and non-verbally. How to solve problems without blaming somebody. How to focus on solutions.

Dancing shows you who you are. I tell couples who come here to prepare for their wedding dance that after twenty lessons, they'll know what their life together will be like.

And in the case of the nursing home residents, dancing takes them beyond their current situation. It lets them remember and relive their youth, for a little while. The very first time I went to a nursing home I participated in one of their socials. And I said, "I'd like to teach you guys how to do some ballroom dancing, so I want to know what music you like and what dances you want to learn." And a lady said to me, "We don't want you to teach us something new. We want you to help us remember how we used *to dance."*

Teachers who do not have their own studio may be employed by a studio, or teach at one (or more) as an independent contractor. Some have no studio or club affiliation and teach out of their homes or at public and private venues to which they pay a *floor fee* – a sum charged for using someone else's dance space.

A teacher may have only a high-school education, or hold an undergraduate or graduate degree in dance, dance-education, or non-dance fields – remember Erica Smith, the Hustling Attorney?

Some teachers have achieved exceptionally high levels of proficiency in their art and compete on the professional level. Some are certified by one of the several international and national organizations that set standards for dance professionals.

In the United States, the organization that sets and oversees teacher certification standards in the ballroom genre is the National Dance Council of America (NDCA). According to its website, NDCA delegates certifying authority to a number of other entities: Arthur Murray International, Dance Teachers Club of Boston, Dance Vision International Dance Association; Fred Astaire Dance of North America; The National Dance Teacher's Association; Pan-American Teachers of Dancing; U.S. Imperial Society of Teachers of Dance and the U.S. Terpsichore Association.

In the ballroom world, many studios both hire experienced professionals *and* grow their own teachers by providing training. Would-be instructors with no prior dance experience must serve what amounts to a rather difficult apprenticeship. They must learn to recognize the signature cadences of dances they will be teaching and master the "lead" *and* "follow" steps and patterns. Newbies are provided with videos and other instructional materials and receive assistance from the more seasoned teachers and often, visiting coaches as well.

Neophytes are expected to learn rapidly. They will be paid little until they can dance well enough to teach beginner-level private lessons and groups. After that, they are paid on an entry-level, per-lesson basis. As they progress, they may be expected to pass certification exams, including verbal and performance elements, at higher and higher levels. Teachers can be certified at the American bronze, silver and gold levels and above, or the very similar European associate, licentiate, and fellow-levels.

Katie Clark enlightened me as to just how much a labor of love dance instruction is for new teachers.

Katie: When I was a brand new teacher at a Fred Astaire studio in California, I was teaching, and I was also given some executive [managerial] and sales responsibility. I was put in charge of new students. I made sure they were placed with the right teacher and handled any problems that came up. If someone came in to buy lessons, I would sit down with them and work out a plan that fit their goals and budget. So, I had a small salary, income from the lessons I taught, and made a commission on my sales. That might sound like it would work out really well, but my take-home paycheck was never any higher than about $500/wk.

Me: Oh, my!

Katie: And, I was trying to compete. I was training and getting coaching. That was expensive and I was in the red all the time. I'd known going in I wouldn't be making much, but I believed I would get to a certain point, professionally and competitively, where I would be able to level up.

Me: But I know teachers who have been in their jobs for years! Also, I asked one experienced instructor point blank whether he made enough money to have a car and a house and a family and he said "yes." So some teachers must eventually make decent money.

Katie: A huge part of how well a teacher does depends on the deal he or she gets at the studio. It depends heavily on what the culture of that studio is. Is it possible to be very successful and make six figures? Yes, it is possible. My partner, Shawn, did it when he worked at Arthur

Murray International. However, the teachers who make that much are either very successful at selling lessons, or they are doing a ton of events, or they are teaching a load of forty lessons a week consistently, which you can only do for so long.

Also, gender is a factor. There are very few female teachers who will ever make it to forty lessons per week, because there aren't enough gentleman students and couples coming through the door. A female teacher is never going to get as many lessons as a male who has, say, three ladies who are all going to be dancing at Emerald [the Emerald Ball – a prestigious competition] next year.

That said, I know many teachers who are very happy at their studio, whether it's franchised or independent. They get a lot of support from the managers and the owner. They have access to continuing education and to coaches that come in. Plus, at a studio, you're not responsible for generating your own student base. You show up to work and people get handed to you...which is a big plus! It's a lot of work to rustle up your own clients. So if teachers are in a studio where they are happy and supported, and feel understood and respected, they're going to stay if they can. And sometimes they get benefits like health care, too.

The big factor, though, is that teachers absolutely love what they do. Yes, it's hard on your body and the hours aren't good, but every teacher I've ever met absolutely loves the job. They care about their students. They care about dancing. They care about teaching. Even veterans who've been around for thirty years still love it. Just as every student who continues has a deeply personal reason why they love dancing, so does every teacher.

Me*: I'd like to think the regard most students have for their teacher is also a part of the reason instructors remain in the field if they possibly can. My own teacher, T.H., is an absolute gem. All his students adore him. I imagine he knows that, and finds it gratifying. However, I worry about what will happen to him as he gets older. There will come a point when he won't physically be able to do what he does now.*

Katie*: Lots of teachers believe they will have their own studio within a certain number of years. The franchises certainly encourage that belief, and for some, it's realistic.*

Teaching people to dance, while simultaneously keeping them entertained and motivated, is not easy. It takes a high level of interpersonal skill combined with encyclopedic knowledge of all the dances in the International and American styles. T.H. enlightened me as to just how *much* information a Ballroom dance instructor must have at his or her command:

Tim Hippert: *There's a lot more to teaching Ballroom than most people outside the dance world might think. We have to be familiar with a tremendous amount of information. Many studios require teachers to become certified [in Tim's case, through NDCA via Arthur Murray International] in the levels at which they teach. New teachers have to work their way up from bronze certification, to silver, and then to gold. In order to get certified at a certain level, we have to know everything about the dances and patterns [steps] taught at that level – which is no simple undertaking.*

The actual certification procedures are rigorous. Teachers spend a lot of time preparing for them. At some levels, a written exam is required, and at all levels, teachers must demonstrate their mastery of both the lead and follow roles in every dance taught at that level. While everyone must be able to show that they know all the dances, they may or may not be required to dance each and every step in every dance, as I was. Some examiners are not that tough. Instead of making the person dance all the patterns, they will choose a certain number at random. Everybody gets quizzed on the various aspects of the demonstrated dance, though: the timing, footwork, and movement that gives the dance its unique character.

My certification exam in full bronze took about ten hours, because I had a really thorough examiner. Most of the time, it takes about six. I had to demonstrate all the steps in twelve different dances – a total of 369 different moves. However, because there are differences in the way each step is danced by leads and follows, teachers must master both roles. I really had to show that I could dance 738 steps. When an instructor gets to the silver and gold levels, and beyond, there will be new sets of patterns to master, and they will be more intricate than the ones in the previous levels.

Wow. Who knew? I thought he just had a good sense of rhythm.

Instructors who teach in street dance genres such as Swing, Hustle, Salsa, may take somewhat different paths into teaching. You will recall that according to Kay Newhouse, teachers in the West Coast Swing Community often emerge from within the culture. No formal certification is required.

Not only must aspiring dance teachers learn to dance, they must learn to *teach* dancing.

While you may think anyone who has mastered a given discipline – particularly a performance discipline – can teach it, that's not always the case. As a college professor, I can tell you schools invest a *lot* of time and money teaching their expert chemists, biologists and mathematicians how to pass along what they know (well, *some* of what they know) to students. Schools realize that unless experts are provided with at least some instruction in the art and science of teaching, they may not be very good at sharing their expertise with others.

An expert no longer has to think about basic procedures. They are carried out automatically, perhaps even unconsciously. In order to *teach* effectively though, experts must be able to explain even simple processes, demonstrate them, and then critique learners' attempts to reproduce them.

In performance disciplines such as dance, that cycle must be repeated over and over (in my case, over and over and over and over) before students catch on. That means in addition to learning to dance and learning to *teach* dancing, new instructors must develop infinite *patience*. Even more challenging in some cases, they must acquire the exceptional interpersonal skills needed to win students' affection, trust and loyalty.

Instructors employed by studios are compensated in a variety of ways. They may be paid an hourly wage, and/or compensated on a per-lesson basis. They may also earn a commission on lesson packages, coaching sessions, and event fees.

Instructors who are independent contractors rather than employees must share a percentage of their earnings with the studio or club at which they teach. Independent teachers are reimbursed directly by their students.

Jameson Kilburn, who with partner Daniel McGee owns Top Hat ballroom studio in Philadelphia and Leola, Pennsylvania, considers his teaching staff valuable assets:

Jameson: Most of our instructors learned to dance at Top Hat. We opened in 1995, so we've had time to grow our own. Most have been with us for double-digits in terms of years. Over the past seventeen years, we've only had four instructors leave. Three moved and we had to fire the other one. Given the turnover in the average dance studio, I'm really proud of that. We try to run things so it's in their best interests to stay. They are independent contractors. Most work for us part-time and work for one or two other studios as well. That's fine with us – we have no non-compete agreements. Most of our teachers are actively competitive dancers and we give them freedom to do that. All we ask is that they get someone to sub for them if they're going to be away. We want them to build a career and we help them do it.

Dance is inherently freeing – we can artistically and visually demonstrate everything we think and feel. So to place restrictions on anything related to dance seems incongruent to me, which is why we have an open-door policy. Staff train twice a week and while Daniel and I run the actual training, we all share information. It's never a "You must do it this way" situation. We also invite students to share their ideas with us. It's a question of great minds coming together, not only to build a better studio but also to support each other in our individual paths.

The non-compete agreements Jameson eschews are legal documents studios often have new teachers sign as a condition of employment. Most such agreements stipulate that teachers who leave the studio may not offer lessons – or contact former students – until a certain number of years (two is common) have elapsed. Geographic limits may also be written into the agreement. For example, a teacher may have to agree not to teach dancing for two years within a 25-mile radius of the studio, or, in the case of a franchised studio, within twenty-five miles of any studio in the chain.

Studios have non-compete agreements because they know students get attached to their teachers. They are well aware that if *your* personal charmer lit out for another studio, you'd be tempted to tag along. Understandably, they don't want to lose business.

Because of dance students' affection for their teachers, and allegiance to them, studios sometimes have *non-fraternization* policies – rules forbidding students and instructors to see each other outside the studio. While some studios forbid any type of fraternization, others are concerned only about *dating*, which could lead to romantic relationships. As a studio owner who prefers to remain anonymous told me:

Studio Owner: *The studio always loses when a teacher becomes romantically involved with a student. If the relationship becomes known, other students get jealous. If it ends, the student leaves the studio. Or, you wind up firing the teacher and the student leaves, anyway.*

The same source said studios that forbid fraternization of *any* sort are likely trying to deter unscrupulous teachers from offering studio students cut-rate lessons on the side.

There is no doubt instructors mean a lot to their students. A number of teachers have left my studio and I've mourned the loss of most, males and females alike, to a degree that surprised me. After all, I didn't really *know* those people. While I saw them a lot – a whole lot – we had no relationship outside the studio, due to the stringent non-frat policy. Nonetheless, our connection around dancing was sufficient to inspire highly positive feelings.

Earle David Reed, the comedian/radio and television personality, described his distress when his teacher left:

Earle: *Another teacher [Justin Howard] came up to tell me last Thursday that my instructor, Elaine, will be leaving soon. I felt a loss immediately – like somebody was going to break up with me. I thought, "Oh, crap, now I have to start over and find someone I'm comfortable with." I mean, I have a lot of rapport with her. It's losing someone close. I know they're young [Elaine and her husband, Luke, also an instructor] and he's going to grad school, and Justin said they want to start a family. That makes perfect sense. Of course they want to do different things…but still, there's that certain selfishness – "Whaddyya mean they're leaving??" So, I'll see how it works out for me.*

Dina Daubenberger, the competition-oriented dancer who also manufactures, rents, and sells dresses, has taken lessons with a number of independent teachers. Dina has thought deeply about why instructors are so important to their students:

Dina: No other situation involves the same kinds of interaction. When you're dancing regularly with someone, it's emotional and it's physical, although of course, there are boundaries. When you dance with an instructor, they get to know you, and give you a different perspective on your life. They live in a different world than you do. They live in a very artistic world, a very feeling world, a very passionate world – and in our daily lives, a lot of that is missing.

Even the music they choose for you can affect your mood…and when you're dancing to that music, and bringing all that feeling and emotion to the movement, it just puts you in a different space. I know this is going to sound crazy to people who don't dance, but that emotion carries over into the rest of your world. It enriches your regular life.

While strong bonds can develop between teachers and students in other settings – I practically worshipped my dissertation advisor when I was in graduate school, and athletes can feel very close to their coaches – the tie seems to be particularly powerful in the context of dance. The likely reason is that dancin' combines three potent ingredients:

- ✓ Psychological intimacy
- ✓ Physical intimacy
- ✓ The pheromone-hormone-chemistry thing

The first ingredient is (mostly one-sided) psychological intimacy. It develops when students and teachers in any discipline work closely together. The teacher is privy to the student's hopes, fears, frustrations and feelings of incompetence and embarrassment. The teacher also witnesses, and rejoices in, the student's breakthroughs and victories.

Ricardo, who you will recall, is a lesser man by 100+ pounds thanks to dancing, alluded to the intimacy between him and his teacher:

Ricardo: *She is in a position to tell me things most people can't or won't. When I start getting into my moods, she'll tell me harsh truths I may not want to hear but need to hear. I might start whining about something and she'll say, "Well, you need to fix it." If I can't get something right away, I can be unpleasant to be around.*

At work, I'm a top dog. I'm a boss. But in that studio, I'm way outside my comfort zone to begin with. And while I'm very forgiving of other people's mistakes, I can't seem to forgive my own. I'm like, "Oh, I'm never gonna get this. I'm so stupid. Blah, blah."

It's crazy, because at work, I give confidence pep talks and tell people they have to believe in themselves. But when it comes to dancing, I can't do that for myself. So, my teacher shares all my ups and downs with me, and that creates a bond. I think for most people, the relationship with the instructor is the most important aspect of the studio.

Good educators accept and support students without judging them – at least overtly – just as good therapists do. The power of psychological intimacy makes students potentially vulnerable to teachers, which is why schools of all kinds forbid members of the teaching staff to date even adult students.

The second ingredient, physical intimacy is an inherent feature of the teacher-student relationship in partner dance – *put your hands on my hips! Feel that? Ok, let's work on Argentine Tango.* As you will remember from Chapter 6, benign physical touch calls forth the bonding hormone oxytocin. Your pets love you, in part, because you *touch* them. Ditto for your children and your spouse.

The *chemistry-hormone-pheromone thing* is a function of the dance-personnel persona.

Most teachers, particularly at high-end studios, look good, smell good, have impeccable manners and treat their customers like gold. Students who take private lessons enjoy the undivided attention of charming, attentive members of the opposite sex to a degree that is hard to come by in real life.

At my studio, for example, the male teachers always have their best foot forward, metaphorically as well as literally. They are immaculately groomed and attired, solicitous, and attentive. They refrain from belching, picking their teeth, and scratching their nether regions. Best of all – unlike most males of my acquaintance – they seem to get that it's all about *me*! They're not really being themselves, of course, but that's what I like about 'em!

Combining psychological intimacy with the physical variety produces what is known in pharmacology as synergism – the power of *both* ingredients is enhanced. Mix in the chemistry-hormone-pheromone thing...and you have the powerful intoxicant I call the Terpsichorean Cocktail. All it needs is to be shaken well – preferably to a Latin beat – and served over cool music.

T.H. is the epitome of a successful dance instructor. Nancy Harrison summed up perfectly the reasons for his success:

Nancy: He's a remarkable young man. He never loses his patience. He's an excellent instructor. I've told him I always feel good after a lesson with him. He's a respectful young man. He treats people with dignity. I think one of the reasons I like him so much is that he treats me the way I want to be treated as a woman. He treats me the way I want a man to treat me outside the studio. I think that's who he really is. I don't think he learned all that at Arthur Murray.

(Maybe, Nance...but maybe not. From what I've heard, T.H. is a former heck-raiser who got spit-shined at A.M.)

Mary Greene is also a satisfied customer when it comes to her teacher, Paul Pietrzak, of Arthur Murray Severna Park:

Mary: He is such a fine young man. He is respectful – and I just love him. I tell him that all the time. And I tell him, "Your mother raised you right." Anybody that said anything against him would have a problem with me. Paul has that kind of personality where I think he really does love people. I don't think he's a phony. I think he's a real people-person. I picked that up the first time I saw him.

Carline Coleman is a Pietrzak fan, as well:

Carline: He's the best! He's a great instructor! He encourages all...and he's nice to look at, too. He's great eye candy. He's understanding. He likes all his students. He doesn't treat anybody any different – we all get treated the same. And he says that he loves his job. He says that all the time. He once told me he feels more like a doctor...and it's true! One day, I left the studio early because somebody had hurt my feelings. He saw me leave, and called me to see what was wrong. That shows you they really care.

Bonnie Stook believes being around the young instructors at her studio is good for her in a number of ways:

Bonnie: *It's kind of fun being taught by instructors [Paul Pietrzak and Alon Pilcher] so much younger. The age thing does not seem to matter. I sometimes look at them and think, "Do you realize how much mileage is on this chassis? You want me to do what?" But yes, they do want us to do it...and eventually, we can!*

I enjoy them. I have no idea what they think about me because they are very professional. They do their job well and very pleasantly. They are friendly and familiar without being intimate beyond dance. Even then, it never gets improper. Although, I think the more we dance with our instructors, the more comfortable and relaxed we get with them.

I would never think of performing moves from some of the more intense Latin dances with a man other than one of the instructors. I tried Argentine Tango [a notoriously steamy dance performed in a close hold] for the first time recently, and thought, "Oh, I'm not going to like this." But it was SO fun! Once in a while, I have to step back and think, "OK, these are very young people. This is a dance and nothing more – snap out of it!"

But it's great fun and good for us. It's just nice to be around these young instructors who have confidence in their abilities, and are so comfortable interacting with men and women of all ages. What a blessing they have found through dance. I'm so pleased for them – that they have that. Because it's going to carry through their lives, and be such an enrichment for them and the people they share themselves with. When they leave, as they occasionally do, it's like losing a family member.

Sharon Murry is equally enthused about dance teachers in general and her own in particular:

Sharon: *The teachers are as proud of that one student who could barely get around but is managing to learn some basic stuff as they are of their gold-level student. They guide you...or pull you...toward creating art...and that has to change you.*

Me: *Oh, absolutely! T.H. drags me out of my comfort zone, kicking and screaming, over and over again. And yet, I rise to those occasions...and every time I do, I surprise myself.*

Sharon: *Yes! That's the mark of a good teacher. He inspires you. He may push you really hard, but you trust him, so you're willing to do it. My very first teacher, Dmitri Naulmov who is still my main teacher, is like that. He is so gracious and kind. He made me feel good right away. He is amazing. His depth of knowledge and his patience are phenomenal. I've never met anyone as patient as he is. He never gets riled up, even when I have to do something 100 times before I can get it right. He is very sought after and gets totally booked up. For the last two years, he's been the top teacher in all the Fred Astaire studios, all over the world. I attribute a lot of the growth I've realized from dance, and my success in competing, to him. He changed my life.*

Charles Sidman, the veteran instructor from Maine, understands perfectly where Nancy, Mary, Carline, Bonnie and Sharon are coming from:

Charles: Being a male dance teacher, I have a lot of female students. I know that for many ladies, being able to dance regularly with a partner who is polite, attentive, caring, and not a jerk...is a confidence-builder and pleasurable experience.

You bet it is, Charlie!

Mr. Sidman presents his own inside-the-industry take on the student-teacher relationship in partner dance:

Charles: I think there is a certain amount of illusion, both deliberate and otherwise, and a willingness to enter into it, on the part of the participants. You have a similar relationship with your doctor and your accountant, but without social interaction...without mutual touch. Bought and paid for intimacy is a part of the business. Obviously a studio or a teacher cannot truly be intimate with 100 different students. Yet, every student has to feel special and appreciated. It's not false, but it's also not the same as when students develop relationships with other students.

I think hero-worship is an additional factor that causes dance students to hold their instructors in high regard. After all, these icons are really good at the art about which we students are so passionate, and it's natural to look up to them. Everyone at my studio absolutely loves watching our teachers perform occasionally, in the studio, and at competitions.

Finally, I think there can be an almost parental vibe between students and the teachers who turned them into dancers. I've heard, "One never forgets one's first teacher" and I have reason to believe that's true. I'm a substantially different person now than three years ago, when I first showed up at Arthur Murray – and I know T.H. had a lot to do with that. While I could be his biological mother in terms of age, it is *he* who created in *me* the dancer who is now such an important part of my identity.

I know I will remember him with gratitude – always.

While some studios discourage teacher-student fraternization, many seem to be okay with it – as long as it doesn't involve dating. For example, Top Hat's Jameson Kilburn has no problem with his instructors hanging out with their students:

Jameson: *We love to travel. Daniel, who founded Top Hat, is a travel agent, so we love to arrange trips for our students. About every eighteen months we go somewhere different. We will end up dancing somewhere, but that's not the purpose of the trip. The purpose is to spend time together and build relationships off the dance floor. We have no restrictions on fraternization with our students. We actually encourage our teachers to become friends with their students and most of us do. We go to birthday parties and weddings and such. We were just invited to a student's daughter's wedding and there were two whole tables of Top Hat people there. When you know people – when you have an actual relationship with them – it makes dancing a lot more fun…a lot more meaningful.*

Cheryl Youtz, whom you met in Chapter 2, is a Top Hat student and appreciates getting to know her teachers well:

Cheryl: *Both Daniel and Jameson were very easy to get to know. It was so comfortable. We consider them our friends. We've had them over for dinner. Daniel is a gourmet cook, and sometimes cooks for his students. If for some reason they would stop being dance instructors, we would have a hard time going somewhere else. When you go to a competition with them, you are the sole focus of their attention.*

In lessons and social dancing, you are their sole focus, too. Top Hat is successful because of Daniel and Jameson. They have poured their hearts and souls into what it has become.

Katie Clark agrees with Jameson that the lengths to which many studios go to prevent departing teachers from "stealing" the studio's students are unnecessary:

Katie: When teachers decide to leave a studio, they are often made to do that very suddenly, and forbidden to tell students where they are going or how to get in touch with them. That's because the studio is afraid their students will follow them.

Me: I know! I hate it when a teacher has been there for a while, and then, at the end of a party, the owner says, "Tonight is so and so's last night." Only that

teacher's personal students are forewarned about the departure. To the others, it comes as a complete surprise. Shock, actually.

Katie*: That is a part of the industry I have a huge problem with. I mean, your students have trusted you, and believed in you and allowed you to have a degree of psychological and physical intimacy with them. So if I'm going to leave and go someplace else, I believe I owe them – personally and professionally – the courtesy of saying, "It has been an honor to work with you. I'm grateful for the time we've had together. I want to let you know where I'm going and what I'll be doing."*

The secrecy around teachers leaving is based on the belief in scarcity – that there aren't enough students to go around. I don't believe that. New students show up at studios all the time. I do believe students are adults in charge of their own dance education. They should feel perfectly free to switch studios or teachers, or take lessons at two studios, or from two teachers, at the same time, if they want to. And, if they want to do that, they shouldn't feel like they have to hide it, but they do feel that way.

For example, I have a female student who's a very strong dancer. When her husband decided he wanted to learn to dance, they started taking couples lessons from me. But, it turned out he wanted more of a social experience. So they started working with a different teacher at a totally social studio, in addition to working with me. When the wife finally told me that, she was SO worried I'd be angry with her. Of course I wasn't angry at all. As a professional, I take lessons with several different coaches. Why should that be any different for students? I just need to know what the student is working on with the other teacher, so I can adjust my lesson plan accordingly. Making people feel like they have to hide what they're doing is toxic.

I was glad to hear from Jameson that just as students are grateful to their teachers, teachers feel proud and fulfilled when they see their labor bearing tangible fruit:

Jameson: For me, the most satisfying aspect of teaching is the feeling that I'm able to pass along a legacy of information about something I love – that I'm passionate about – to people I care about. That is very precious to me. I have been fortunate to have amazing teachers and coaches who have taught me a lot and I want to pass that on. I have one student who is home-grown in that she has been taught only by me and other teachers in our studio. She competes in pro-am events with me, has climbed the competitive ranks and is currently undefeated in her division. She recently found a partner and will be going pro herself soon. The fact that I had a hand in helping someone succeed in this path is enormously satisfying to me. It gives me an incredible sense of pride. I also feel it balances the scales in terms of karmic law – some of my coaches really went out on a limb for me and taught me when I couldn't pay them much. That was done with the understanding I would one day pass that along. Dance is definitely a mentor-protégé business – like any of the fine trades.*

Jameson also waxed eloquent about the multi-faceted challenges many students (and all instructors) face in a dance studio:

Jameson: It was said to me, when I first trained to become a partner dance teacher, that 80% of what we do is therapy and the other 20% is teaching dance. I laughed at that, and thought, "That's ridiculous." But now I believe we're the most underpaid psychiatrists out there! I now realize that as a teacher, I have a hands-on look at couples and how they relate to each other. People learn in different ways. Our personality traits come out when we learn something new. If a student has control issues, I can see that in the way they approach dancing. If they have anxiety issues…I'm able to see that. And separation anxiety –

you can see that when a couple is learning partner dance and doesn't want to dance with other people.

Understanding how a person prefers to receive praise – and when they prefer to receive it – is important. I've had students who get offended if I tell them they're doing an excellent job, because they know they're not dancing as well as I do. Other students feel I'm not appreciative of their work if I don't commend every little milestone. I take all that into consideration when teaching. Individual differences are something to which I've become attuned. You can learn a lot from books – Myers-Briggs personality styles, and the Five Love Languages *– I've learned a lot that way.*

Teaching dance is the easy part. The hard thing is dealing with the emotional head games people put themselves through. Dance is challenging on a number of levels. Someone who has walked into a dance studio for the first time must not only understand they have a body, but move it in a manner that is completely unnatural to them. They have to put themselves in awkward positions – sometimes very intimate positions – with a partner. A lot of people are not comfortable with any of that at first.

They will look at themselves, and watch themselves move, in front of a full-length mirror. Many people have allowed daily routine to alter their body in a way they're not aware of until they start looking in that mirror. Dance makes us aware of our body's limitations and provides an optimal environment in which we can overcome them, at least to some degree, if we choose. If we don't like something, we change it. If we don't want to put the work into changing it, we accept it.

One of my students lost an extreme amount of weight – maybe 125 pounds – not only from dancing, but also diet and exercise. He says the part dancing played was making him more aware of himself. Until he came to the studio, he had never taken a really good look at himself in a mirror.

Having both body awareness and the decision power to change something or accept it, gives people an ownership of their bodies that is important. The awareness that dance fosters is about more than just the body – it's about the mind and soul, too. Gaining understanding of how the three are connected is one of the biggest benefits of what we teach. That understanding gives a person strength and confidence in a way few other things do.

Being a good dance teacher is not easy. It is physically and mentally challenging and calls for a bottomless reservoir of perseverance and tact. Charles Sidman recalls how difficult it was to lead one balky horse to the water he badly needed:

Charles: Just last week, there was a gentleman in our group class who was very serious about his dancing. He'd studied with some good people. He collected tapes. My take on some of the dancing – and my way of presenting it – was different from his…and he was a little bit – oh, more than a little bit – affronted and bothered by that. It threatened his view of the universe and the competence of his former teachers.
Throughout the two hours we spent together, I tried to remain positive and respectful of his teachers and influencers while communicating there are many different flavors in the spectrum. We take away different things from different teachers. It's a choice how we put it all together. It's a growth experience to see that what we're doing is not the way, it's a way.

Jameson Kilburn told me how incredibly demanding his job is, from a physical standpoint:

Jameson: The shortest teaching day I have is seven hours, dancing pretty continuously sometimes without a break. On Fridays, I generally have five private lessons in a row with students who are advanced competitors. With them, I dance at a pretty high level, almost constantly, for five hours. There's no food or breaks. A stretch like that is really taxing. At the end of it, I'm tired and sweaty and feel as though I just ran a marathon...and I have

another two hours to go with other students. If I'm preparing for a competition, I rehearse two to four hours, three days a week, before beginning my regular duties at the studio. I'll start at 10 a.m. and go till one or two. Then teach from 2:30 in the afternoon until ten at night. I also do yoga and calisthenics most mornings. When I was younger, the regimen included going to the gym, but I'm slacking now.

Unfortunately, as Jameson points out, dance teachers don't generally get the respect they deserve...except, of course, from their students – who understand and appreciate what they do.

Jameson: People think teaching dance is a frivolous occupation that adds little benefit to society or the world. Some think we are dance teachers because we couldn't do anything else. But I have a degree in international business. I chose dance. My dad jokes that I'd make more money in my fallback career than in my actual job. I often get calls asking if I'll do lessons and demonstrations for free. I can't think of another profession in which people would even think of asking you to prepare ahead of time, put on a costume, drive to a place and perform a service – all for nothing.

Katie Clark also chose dancing over a more lucrative and prestigious profession.

Katie: *I took my first ballroom dance class when I was a freshman in college, and I was blown away. I thought it was the greatest thing ever. I was not a dance major, though. It was just something I loved doing. So I danced my way through college and when I went to graduate school in England, I stopped dancing for about 7 years. Then, I moved back to California and wanted to start dancing again. I lived up the street from a Fred Astaire studio and so one day I went in to see about lessons and things took off from there.*

Me*: Katie, before we get into the Fred Astaire experience, I want to backtrack a bit and get more info about your education. You mentioned college and then grad school. Being a professor myself, I'm interested in what schools you attended and what you majored in.*

Katie*: I went to Tulane University in New Orleans and majored in History, Latin, French and Medieval Studies.*

Me*: Four majors?!*

Katie*: Yep. I was interested in all those things. I did my grad work in Medieval History. I had a Marshall scholarship, so I went over to Oxford in England and got my MST there.*

Me*: Oxford! Holy cow! What's an MST?*

Katie*: It's like an MA (Master's of Art), basically. It's a master's in Historical Research.*

Me: *I'm duly impressed. So, back to Fred Astaire. What happened there?*

Katie: *I told them I already knew how to dance and wanted to work on technique, which I did. After about a year, I got interested in competing, but that plus the lessons, was getting too expensive. I was working at Cal Tech [California Institute of Technology] as an instructor on a post-doc [post-doctoral] fellowship, and not making much money.*

Me: *Post-doc fellowship? You earned a doctorate over in England?*

Katie: *Yes. I hold the English equivalent of a Ph.D. Anyway, I was already helping out informally with instruction at the studio. I was doing some leading if they needed a leader in a group class, and working on the sidelines with students who were having difficulty. So, I approached the studio owner about doing some formal teaching in exchange for lessons, and he agreed that if I taught four private lessons I could take one.*

So I worked at Cal Tech during the day and taught at Fred Astaire in the evening. In the summer of 2012, my fellowship ended and I started applying for jobs in academia. I got a couple of offers from universities for tenure track positions. But, after a LOT of hard thinking, I realized dancing was what I truly loved and I became a full-time dance instructor instead.

Me: *Katie, earlier you mentioned you have your own studio now. How did that come about?*

Katie: *I worked at Fred Astaire for about a year. In February of 2013, another teacher there, Shawn Groth, and I decided we were going to leave the studio and do our own thing. Shawn had been dancing much longer than I and was very experienced. At one time, he was the top specialist – I mean in the entire country – at Arthur Murray International. He absolutely loves working with new students.*

Me: *How did you and Shawn manage to make a go of it on your own?*

Katie: *We started by doing some consulting work at a large swing-oriented independent studio in a different county. That studio would have 200-300 people coming through the door to dance socially, six to* *seven nights a week. They'd have loads of teachers wandering around, but not much structure. So, Shawn and I helped the owner with some organizational concerns, taught students, and did teacher-training. We did the consulting for a couple of months, and that was really great and a lot of fun, but we knew we didn't have a long-term future there.*

So we started to teach independently and in February of 2014 we opened our "studio," Connected Dancer, but decided not to have a brick and mortar space. We didn't want to be confined geographically and didn't want the liability of having our own building. We knew there were lots of independent studios in Southern California in which we could rent floor space as we needed it. So that's what we do. We also teach in peoples' homes.

Me: *Do you rent floor space for a set amount or a percentage of the group or private lesson fee?*

Katie: *It's a set fee. I've seen it range from ten bucks to thirty bucks for an hour. Thirty is too high. I wouldn't pay that. Twelve, fifteen bucks for an hour is standard. Our business is doing well. Shawn has his client base and I have mine, but as we often teach as a team, we know each other's students. If he's sick, I'll cover his lessons and vice-versa.*

Me: *Katie, you and Shawn named your studio The Connected Dancer. Did you have any particular reason, beyond the obvious, for choosing that name?*

Katie: *We chose it because dancing involves so much more than moving your feet in a pattern to a certain rhythm. The magic of partner dancing is how it helps people connect with themselves in a way they may never have before. They become more aware of their body – its level of fitness, balance, strength, flexibility and agility. And, they find they can improve all of that. People also become better acquainted with themselves emotionally – they may be surprised at how they react to trying to learn something that's hard at first, or to dancing with people they don't know well.*

People can use dancing however they want to. Some choose to focus on improving their physical stamina – maybe to be able to get through three Cha Chas in a row without being ready to pass out. Or maybe you really care about being able to tell stories with your body, or maybe what does it for you is getting to reconnect to that part of yourself that likes goofing around, or wearing sparkly dresses.

At Connected Dancer, we believe every student we have the privilege to teach is a special individual with a unique life story. We believe it's our job as teachers to help them connect more strongly to the parts of themselves they already love, and also connect to the parts of themselves that are challenging. Beyond that, our job is to help them connect better to the music, to a partner, and to reach whatever physical, emotional or performance goals they've set for themselves.

Me: *That's beautiful, Katie. I love it!*

Katie: *Both Shawn and I know firsthand what dancing can do for people. We both have good reasons for saying dancing saved our lives. Becoming dance teachers has forced us to examine our own humanity. How we bring ourselves to people and deal with them.*

Me: *What do you get back from your students, Katie?*

Katie: *So-o-o much! I've always loved teaching. Even as an academic, I was on fire about teaching. There is nothing like it. It's the greatest thing in the world. I could be having the worst day and knowing I'm going to get to go teach makes it better.*

Also, Shawn and I have students who are around the age of our parents. Historically – although that is changing now – Ballroom has attracted a demographic that's a little bit older – forty-five and up. So, we get to work with people who have a lot of life experience. Some are are also inquisitive and brilliant, and lead complex, fascinating lives. We learn a lot from our students. That they are willing to place their trust in us is extremely gratifying and we take that responsibility seriously.

I also find it fulfilling when people learn to be present in their own bodies. I love helping someone discover his or her own immense potential. To me, seeing them realize they can do something they didn't think was possible is such a gift. To be in the room when that happens is a WOW!

Shawn and I will be sitting in the car, or on our patio, after a lesson in which a student made an amazing breakthrough and we'll be like, that's insane, what they did! That's insane! For example, sometimes a couple will achieve a level of connectedness and communication on the dance floor they've never experienced before in their entire relationship and that will change the relationship. To know we played a part in that is phenomenal.

Lessons

People have a wide range of reasons for taking dance lessons. Some wish only to prep for their wedding dance, while others want to become proficient social dancers, or want to compete, or both. Many are looking for an enjoyable form of exercise or seeking a social outlet. A few – like Kevin Sand, whose moving story of his battle with social anxiety you read in Chapter 8 – are hoping to overcome a personal challenge.

Many studios and clubs offer low-priced introductory lesson packages that allow new students to get a taste of dancing so they can decide whether they wish to pursue it. What happens next for those who decide to continue depends on the studio or club.

At the two major franchised Ballroom chains, and at some independent ballroom studios, students are asked to commit, by signing a contract, to a program of instruction tailored to personal goals. They are asked to identify several dances on which they want to focus during a series of private lessons, and pay for them up front or on a monthly plan.

Dance studio contracts have the same advantages as the gymnasium/health club variety. One advantage is you're less likely to decide, on a whim, to skip a private or group lesson, because you've already paid for it. Also, many studios that use the contract system are a bit like Disneyland – once you've purchased your admission ticket (your lesson program), you are free to go on all the rides. The cost of the private lessons covers all, or at least some, group lessons and parties. Moreover, you will likely be free to use the studio's floor for practice.

Dance studio contracts are not binding. If you sign one and later decide to withdraw, your money will be refunded, although you may have to pay a modest fee. Studios and clubs that do not use contracts offer lessons and parties on a pay-as-you-go basis. Discounted lesson packages are usually available.

In Ballroom, the actual steps and patterns of the dances you learn will be based on one of several dance syllabi. Arthur Murray International and Fred Astaire, Inc. have their own, which they make available to their franchisees. Owners of non-franchised studios and clubs, and instructors working independently, can purchase syllabi from organizations such as DVIDA (Dance Vision International Dance Association), NDCA (National Dance Council of America), ISTD (Imperial Society of Teachers of Dance) or the USISTD (United States Imperial Society of Teachers of Dance).

While the various Ballroom dance syllabi differ slightly in terms of the names and execution of patterns and steps, they all provide instruction in the essential elements of partner dance: frame, connection, movement and rhythm. Thus, an accomplished "follow" who took lessons based on the DVIDA syllabus will be able to cope perfectly well with a "lead" who learned at a Fred Astaire or Arthur Murray studio. Syllabi are also available in some of the street dance genres.

Private and group dance lessons last anywhere from forty to sixty minutes. Whether you take a lesson as a single individual or as part of a couple, the charge is the same – you're paying for the teacher's time. During private lessons, the instructor will introduce the basics of frame and connection, demonstrate steps and patterns of the dance *du jour* and then coach you as needed.

Group lessons are similar. Teachers demonstrate steps and patterns, then coach students as they pair off and try to emulate the instructor, first without music and then with. Students generally rotate from one partner to another. Couples are allowed to remain together if they wish. While private instruction shortens the learning curve, many people take only group lessons.

If there are more female than male students (or vice-versa) other instructors may step in and partner up with the extra students. Dance teachers can both lead and follow. Occasionally one will get the two roles mixed up – that's always good for a laugh.

If additional instructors are not available, a rotation system will be established so everyone gets to dance.

As students advance they are introduced to the more subtle elements of good dancing – better frame, enhanced connection, more precise footwork and timing. They will also be introduced to what is known as *styling* – using arms, fingers, and movement to really bring a particular genre of dance to life and imbue it with its signature look and feel.

If I had a strong point – which I don't – styling wouldn't be it. My arm movements tend to resemble those of a defective windmill. My version of the *come hither* look for which ladies strive in the more sultry dances would better suit a virgin who finds herself at a Hell's Angels slumber party.

Dancing will never bore you.

You will be able to work toward increasing levels of competence. There will always be a carrot dangling – seemingly just out of reach.

In the U.S., dancers' expertise is ranked from lowest to highest according to the following designations: newcomer, beginner, bronze 1, 2, 3 & 4, silver 1-4, and (finally!) gold 1-4. Post-gold-4 dancers may be referred to as *open* dancers or by other terms, depending on the studio. Some organizations use ranking only with students interested in competition.

Other studios, clubs and street dance organizations don't use the bronze-silver-gold schema described above. They may advertise private and group lesson series in terms of the type of student for which they are appropriate – the use of descriptors such as b*eginner,* i*ntermediate* or *advanced* is common.

Regardless of what terms are used to mark progress, dancing will continue to challenge you. Just as you begin to feel really comfortable at one level of accomplishment, your teacher will drop-kick you out of your comfort zone.

You'll be promoted to the next level.

Parties and Outings

Most dance organizations provide social dances, sometimes called *parties*, for their students/members, and sometimes for the general public. Parties may be held in the studio or at various outside venues (restaurants, clubs etc.). Alcohol may or may not be provided or allowed. It is common for students/members to bring, or be able to purchase, snacks and food.

Alas, my own studio spikes the punch only at our Christmas party and on Arthur's birthday – and even then, the parsimonious pour would win a smile from Carrie Nation.

The etiquette observed at parties sponsored by Ballroom-oriented studios or groups is a holdover from earlier centuries. Women are still referred to as *ladies,* and men as *gentlemen.* Gentlemen are encouraged to properly invite a lady to dance, and then escort her back to her seat afterward – as opposed to ditching her to dodge traffic in the middle of the floor.

Instructors commonly beseech ladies to allow them to "steal" a dance – a flattering turn of phrase which allows me to imagine, for a millisecond, I'm being purloined from the proximity of some adoring swain. Ahhh…my romantic heart flutters, even as my feminist brain reminds it that such niceties flowered during an age when women were mostly powerless.

Still – and I'm embarrassed to admit this – the antique conventions of Ballroom beguile me with their quaintness. That they have been all but abandoned by the relatively less gender-conscious youth culture is, I know, something to be celebrated in the name of progress.

And yet….

One of the big differences between a relatively small dance club or studio and a large independent or franchised studio is that the latter is more likely to have a goodly number of instructors on hand to dance with students at parties. The costs associated with maintaining a large staff is a major reason why lessons at large independent or franchised studios are fairly expensive.

If you are a single female – excuse me – *lady* thinking of taking lessons at a particular studio, you may wish to inquire whether instructors will be available to dance with you at parties. If the answer is "No," best to inquire next about the number of single males who typically show up and whether it is customary for women to ask men to dance. In most places, it is.

Happily, some gentlemen who have partners of their own go out of their way to invite unaccompanied ladies onto the floor:

Linda Weed: My partner asks other women to dance, and that's fine with me and good for him. It builds his confidence as a dancer. He dances with some women who are better dancers than he, and are able to point a few things out to him in a nice way…a way that's constructive and doesn't make him feel bad. As a new leader, he sometimes feels awkward about dancing with other women because he doesn't want to be judged.

Becca Hirsch told me her husband John was reluctant to dance with other women at first, but soon got over that:

Becca: When we first started dancing, I'd try to get John to dance with other ladies, and he'd say, "I didn't come here to dance with other people." Now, he dances with everybody and I have to remind him to dance with me.

However, not all gentlemen are thoughtful – or brave – in that way. Would that the *Hand-Book of Etiquette*, published in 1861, were better known and more widely followed: *"If gentlemen go to balls, they should dance. It is a great breech of etiquette to stand idling and sauntering while ladies are waiting for an invitation to dance."*

Yea, verily!

In the process of conducting research for this book, I stumbled upon a phenomenon of which I'd been unaware: the platonic dance partnership. It seems that in the dance world, it's common for men and women to have relationships based on a combination of non-romantic friendship and dancing – or just dancing. Nancy Harrison described a relationship of the latter type that was very fulfilling for her:

Nancy: When I started taking lessons in upstate New York at an independent studio, there was a physician who had been ballroom dancing with his wife for most of their marriage. She developed Lou Gehrig's Disease and ended up bed-bound. He continued to go to the studio for lessons. It provided him opportunities to dance and be social. When I started taking lessons, we eventually paired off as dance partners. I gained an experienced partner who was absolutely delightful to dance with, and I think he liked dancing with me, too.

What was interesting was that when I would go to dance class with him, we barely said anything to each other except "Hello," and then, "See you next week." We never got to know each other on a personal level. But just the experience of being in, for lack of a better word, partnership with a man was joyful for me. There was just something about getting lost in the dance with a man that made me feel so much better about myself. It was validating for me as a woman.

Nancy's experience was by no means unique. Such relationships are common in the dance world. I know two young people who dance regularly together. Both have romantic partners who are non-dancers. Another situation involves two married (to other people!) individuals who go dancing together with their spouses' full knowledge and consent.

If you're interested in acquiring a dance pal, check out www.DancePartner.com.

The "connection" you make on that website won't lead to blood tests and a lengthy course of antibiotics.

13

Where Classy Meets Sassy:

Amateur Competition

I do not try to dance better than anyone else. I only try to dance better than myself. ~Mikhail Baryshnikov

Like golfers, bowlers, tennis players, runners, squash enthusiasts, and ping-pong people, dancers get to test themselves – and show off – in competitive events, a.k.a. *comps*. Comps range from small, high-fun/low-stakes affairs to prestigious international events at which world championships are decided.

Large regional, national and international events include amateur, pro-am and professional competition. Smaller local and regional events feature only the amateur and pro-am variety.

In amateur competition, a couple is comprised of two amateurs. In pro-am events, amateurs compete in partnership with their teachers, although only the student is judged.

Comps are held in all partner dance genres – Ballroom, West Coast Swing, Urban Dance, etc. The organization, studio, club, group or individual that put a given comp together is called the *organizer*. Competitions in the various genres are run according to rules established by a governing organization in that genre or style. To ensure a level playing field, competitors are segregated according to proficiency level and age.

Ballroom

The National Dance Council of America (NDCA) oversees all official Ballroom competition in the United States. Organizations such as USA Dance (which refers to ballroom competition as *DanceSport*), Fred Astaire, Inc., Arthur Murray International, and their affiliates, organize competitions run according to NDCA guidelines.

Ballroom comps are relatively swanky affairs that feature several types of events, the most numerous being *single-dance heats*. A single-dance heat is a one-and-a-half to two minute period during which multiple couples take the floor and execute the same dance style (Waltz, for example) without knowing ahead of time what the music will be. They will be scrutinized by several judges who independently rank them. The judges' combined rankings are then used to determine the overall heat placements.

Stef Lein, a seasoned ballroom comp veteran from Arizona, provided details about how the winning couple in a heat is determined:

Stef: Each judge places the couples first, second, third and so on, and these placements are tabulated. This is why you see numbers such as 33221 included in media coverage of competitions featuring well-known couples. In the 33221 example, the 3-3 means two judges placed the couple third. The 2-2 means two judges placed them second and the 1 means one judge placed them first. The couple with the most firsts wins and the other rankings follow the same pattern.

Hopefully the rankings will agree somewhat, indicating that the judges were generally on the same page regarding the quality of the couple's performance. Sometimes, though, they vary widely. A couple can miss a higher placement, because of just one judge's opinion. Competitors can often obtain their score sheets online after the competition, to see how a particular judge placed them. Dancers who know the individual judge's predilections – some judges are known to focus on top lines or footwork or overall presentation – can gain insight into areas to work on.

About now, you may well be envisioning a row of judges seated at a dais, wielding paddles with numbers on them, à la Len and company on *DWTS*.

Nope.

While at ballroom comps, judges are indeed seated at a dais for single-dance heats (to be explained shortly), they usually walk the perimeter of the floor for multi-dance heats. They also submit their rankings on placement sheets designed for that purpose. No paddles are involved. Moreover, after witnessing an exceptional performance, they neither tear-up, à la Carrie Ann, nor provide extravagant *Brunoesque* praise.

The competitors in each heat will be at the same general ability level. Depending on the organizer, proficiency may be designated in terms of *newcomer* plus those "metal" indicators – *associate bronze* through *full gold* – or, in some genres, novice, pre-championship and championship.

A single-dance heat will be listed in the competition's schedule according to proficiency level, dance style, and whether the heat is closed or open. Here's an example, using a "metal" proficiency indicator:

Heat #38, full bronze Waltz closed.

Closed means dancers may execute only steps and patterns consistent with (or below) the level at which they are dancing. For example, in a full-bronze heat, only patterns listed in the bronze-3 and bronze-4 (or easier moves from the bronze 2 or 1) sections of whichever syllabus applies may be executed.

In *open* heats, anything – well, almost anything – goes. Lifts are allowed only in certain kinds of events. But if dancers can manage steps one level above their official ability level, they are free to perform them.

In our example, *Heat #38, full bronze Waltz closed,* some competitors might be bronze-3 dancers, while others might be bronze-4. (You will recall that levels 3 and 4 comprise the *full* category in all the "metal" categories, while levels 1 and 2 comprise the *associate* category). It is possible, therefore, that in Heat #38, a bronze-3 dancer might wind up placing higher than a bronze-4 dancer. A complicating factor is that competitors are allowed to enter heats above their actual level of proficiency, to see how they do against more experienced dancers. A bronze-4 dancer who decided to dare an associate silver heat just might place higher than one or more of the silver-level dancers.

Sound pretty simple thus far?

Wait. It gets more complicated.

While dancers participating in a heat will be at the same general proficiency level, they can be in different *age categories*. In competitions run according to NDCA rules, the adult age categories are as follows:

- ✓ Adult (19-34 yrs.)
- ✓ Senior 1 (35-44 yrs.)
- ✓ Senior II (45-54 yrs.)
- ✓ Senior III (55 and older)

You didn't realize the golden years started at age 35, did you?

In single-dance heats, only competitors in the same sex and age category are compared. For example, my current – and likely perpetual – ability level is bronze-3. When I enter a full-bronze heat, I'm judged against only the *other* Senior III women in the heat. The Senior II ladies would be judged only against one another, and so on. Thus, although competitors in the same age range are often grouped in heats, it is possible that two or more ranges will be represented in the same one. If that happens, there may be multiple 1st, 2nd, etc. placements.

I told you it was complicated.

Heat results are seldom announced immediately, as it takes time for the judges' placements to be tabulated and final results determined.

Computations are handled by officials known as *scrutineers*. (There's something vaguely smutty about that word.)

At more formal competitions, placements are announced publicly, in batches, usually during breaks in the competition. At less formal ones, such as studio showcase events, rankings may be conveyed to participants privately. Students' scores in all their heats are tabulated and provided in writing to their instructors, who eventually pass the news along. In my case, they take pains to do so in an appropriately gentle, consoling manner.

In addition to single-dance heats, competitors may also sign up for *multi-dance* heats in which two, three or more dances in a certain style are performed sequentially. For example, in a smooth two-dance heat, dancers may be required to execute dances such as Waltz, Foxtrot or Tango sequentially. What makes it interesting is that competitors don't know in advance which two, out of all the smooth dances, will be required.

All-arounds are another variety of multi-dance heats. In all-around competition, dancers sequentially demonstrate mastery of randomly chosen dances from *both* the International Standard/American Smooth and Latin/American Rhythm categories. More advanced dancers can choose to compete in multi-dance competition involving as many as nine or ten rounds, which is physically taxing as the heats come one right after the other.

The footnoted video of a professional championship event will give you an idea of what multi-dance competition is like.[76] The results are announced right away. How would *you* place those spectacular couples?

---

[76] Watch the championship video at: http://youtu.be/EF78-SHLg_g

Scholarship is the highest level of pro-am competition and the only level in which a monetary prize – in the form of a "scholarship" fund paid to the student's studio – is awarded.

Official, large comps may feature an array of amateur and pro-am events billed as *championships*. For example, among the championship events listed in the 2014 schedule for the DanceSport *Colorado Star Ball* were American Smooth one-dance, Senior American Smooth three-dance, and World Closed Smooth Dance-Sport Pro-Am. Similar championship-level events are held at other large comps, including those sponsored by Arthur Murray International, and Fred Astaire, Inc. A couple who wins such an event will claim it as an impressive victory – and perhaps a stepping stone to even more prestigious recognition.

Serious amateur and pro-am competitors often seek high ranking on the regional or national level. To achieve it, they participate throughout the year in competitions that are part of an official annual circuit. Their placements in each event within each comp are tracked, and at the end of the year, an organization such as USA Dance will announce its overall regional and national rankings.

A good-sized competition may involve many hundreds of events spread over two or more days. Dancers with endurance and good feet, not to mention sufficient $$ to cover all those entry fees, may enter 200 heats or more. Participants can rack up that many over the course of a comp by choosing to compete in many different dance styles (Waltz, etc.), entering open and closed single and multi-dance heats, dancing in heats above their actual ability level, and entering heats one age category below their own.

Judges must weigh a variety of factors when evaluating the quality of a couple's dancing: frame, footwork, "lines" (top-line, leg-line), musicality, artistry, athleticism, grooming and overall partnership. They have very little time to decide order of placement in a heat that may last only a minute and a half. That is why the lead's *floor craft* – strategic positioning and maneuvering – is important, and getting noticed immediately is crucial:

Cherella: *You have to do everything you can to make sure the judge will be looking your way when you're doing your best move – that's a skill in itself. You need to make a favorable impression right away – when you walk onto the floor, and when you close [get into dance frame] with your partner. Judges who get the impression there might be something special about you will look at you more often. Even if you fall on the floor, how you get up determines whether you get points added or taken away. You need to have in mind, "I want to win this damn thing!" Not that you're necessarily better than other people, but that you're gonna TRY harder than anybody else. They [judges] see that. They know you*

know what you're there for. They want to see people who are obviously giving it everything they've got.

Entering heats and all-arounds is not the only way dancers get to compete. They can also do *solo routines*. A routine is a one-and-a-half to two-minute choreographed dance sequence designed around a particular piece of music. Routines can feature one or a combination of dance styles, such as Waltz, and are performed at all levels of expertise.

Routines can be nerve-wracking.

The choreography, created by teachers or visiting coaches, is usually challenging, which is why couples rehearse endlessly. They know when performance time comes, they will be on the floor alone – as the term *solo* implies – with all eyes on *them*.

Moreover, unexpected challenges can arise:

Anton: When we did the Las Vegas Superama for the first time, they had 500 entries – way more than expected – and they ran out of room in the hotel's main ballroom. So, they moved all the rhythm solos to the Queen Nefertiti nightclub lounge, which is not only small, but is a pit – like an ancient Roman amphitheater – with 6-foot high walls around it and big, round columns positioned at four places around the perimeter. The floor itself is concrete, with Egyptian hieroglyphics carved into it in one-inch deep grooves. We were dancing a Cha Cha routine in there, and our feet kept getting caught in the grooves. It was all we could do to keep from falling.

Couples who needed room for their runaways [multi-step forward or backward movement] had to contend with the six-foot wall that surrounded the pit. They wound up running up the access ramps in order to get all the moves in their routine in. You can't anticipate stuff like that. And if you can't adapt to it instantaneously, you're not going to perform well.

Competitors who have distinguished themselves at a formal or informal competition are rewarded with a trophy of some kind, usually at the banquet that follows most comps. Depending on the organizer, awards may include Top Female Student, Top Male Student, Top Couple, and Best Routine in all ability categories (newcomer, associate-bronze, full-bronze, etc.). Top Teacher and Top School are also customarily recognized.

Chris Lindy, an experienced Ballroom instructor and pro-competitor who currently teaches at Arthur Murray Lemoyne, Pennsylvania, enlightened me as to how award recipients are chosen:

Chris: *Winners are determined by a point system based on heat placements. Dancers get three points for each heat in which they place 1st, two points for coming in 2nd, and one point for coming in 3rd. In some comps, dancers also get a point for each heat they enter. At the end of the comp, the points are tallied and the honorees determined. The teacher whose students garnered the most points is designated Top Teacher and the Top School award is bestowed on the same basis.*

Many ballroom studios hold informal events, sometimes billed as *showcases*, at which students can show off their dancing (think piano recital) for family, friends and each other and also receive private feedback on their performance from judges. In addition to conventional heats and routines, such events often feature *spotlights*. In spotlights, amateur or pro-am couples perform a dance style, for the duration of a conventional heat, with no other couple on the floor. Awards, similar to those bestowed at comps, are often presented at the end of showcase events.

Ballroom competitions and showcases typically offer more than just the opportunity to compete. There are also cocktail parties, banquets and wonderful exhibitions put on by the participating studios' teaching staff and often, a touring, high-profile professional couple as well.

Large competitions feature professional as well as amateur and pro-am contests. Amateurs can risk permanent damage to their egos by watching Ballroom's gods and goddesses enchant and bedazzle.

Think I'm exaggerating? Two-time Latin world-champions Yulia Zagoruychenko and Riccardo Cocci melt the floor with a sublime solo Rumba.[77]

In *this* Rumba heat, the camera follows Yulia and Riccardo – but all the pros look amazing.[78]

---

[77] Watch the first Yulia/Riccardo Rumba video at: http://youtu.be/LtzyOJcwN9o
[78] Watch the second Yulia/Riccardo Rumba video at: http://youtu.be/TpdIp6Re0lQ

I like Latin a lot.

Who doesn't?

But it's *Ballroom* that has my heart. I'm enraptured by its romantic, fairy-tale gorgeousness.

You'll know what I mean when you see this stunning Waltz by reigning (as of this writing) Professional World Ballroom champions Katusha Demidova (oh, those Russian women!) and Arunas Bizokas. I see Katusha as a princess-swan, gliding in eternal synchrony with Arunas – her perfect prince.[79]

Don't be discouraged. Unless you're still playing with dolls or action-figures, amateur and pro-am competition is the only kind in which you'll ever be involved, at least in the ballroom genre. Most high-

---

[79] Watch the Katusha/Arunas video at: http://youtu.be/xEWdj-NZD2Q

level professionals, particularly those who grew up in Europe, hit the floor for the first time when barely out of diapers. American-born pros tend to start a bit later, usually by their early teens,[80] but still have a substantial head-start on the rest of us. I've included pro-vids in this tome to class it up a little…and make sure you'll remain appropriately humble about *your* dancing.

There's no need to thank me.

West Coast Swing

MADjam (The Mid-Atlantic Dance Jam), held in the Washington, D.C. area, is a well-known West Coast Swing event that draws enthusiasts from all over the country and includes opportunities for competition. Kay Newhouse, the way-smooth Westie you met in the last chapter, filled me in on how competition works in her genre:

Kay: Our events are a mix of workshops, private lessons, competition and social dancing. In fact, our social dancing goes on all night – typically till six or seven in the morning. We may call an event a comp, but the focus for most people is the social dancing. We are a very informal, social community. At events, we wear regular clothes – no costumes except for routines – the emphasis is on getting to know new people. It's a very friendly community. Even serious competitors are supportive of one another. Jack and Jill is the most widespread form of competition in West Coast, although we have others as well.

---

[80] McMains, J. (2006). Glamor Addiction: inside the American ballroom dance industry. Middletown: CT. Wesleyan University Press.

Me: What's a Jack and Jill?

Kay: You enter on your own, without a partner. Then, you are randomly paired with another competitor and you dance with that person. You don't know the music ahead of time. Jack and Jills are usually danced in heats in the lower levels, but in the upper levels the finals might be done as spotlights [one couple on the floor at a time]. You might switch among three or four randomly chosen partners in preliminary rounds, where you are judged as an individual. Then, you are assigned one partner for the final round, and judged and placed as a couple.

Me: So, in Jack and Jill competition, you may never have danced with your partner before in your life??

Kay: Exactly.

Me: Yikes! That's intense!

Kay: Yes, but it's also fun! There's an element you can't plan for, and that was meant to sort of parallel the experience of social dancing. Jack and Jills are about impromptu lead and follow choreography. You make it up and go along. It's not planned. You do occasionally draw a partner you've danced with before, but there's no guarantee. Jack and Jills are what most people enter – from newcomers all the way to people who've been dancing for a long time.

    We also have a category called Strictly Swing, or Strictlies, which is similar, but you enter those with a partner you know. You don't know the music, though. We also have pro-am competition in which people dance with their teacher. Finally, we have competitive routines. There are two categories for that: Classic and Showcase. Classic is feet-on-the-floor, and in Showcase, you can have lifts. Routine competition is not as popular as Jack and Jill. At a given comp, you might have 12 routine couples and 300 Jack and Jill entries.

Me: Do judges have to be certified by an organization?

Kay: There's no judging-certification process. The organizer of a specific event and the head judge will choose a few people they feel are competent to judge and invite them to do that. I've just started judging at events myself. The head judge in our D.C. area, Dawn Garrish, did *have an apprentice program that she put me and a few other people in, but that was her doing and the event organizer's. It wasn't anything really official or organized beyond our area.*

Me: *What organizations set the rules for West Coast comps?*

Kay: *Comps can be independent, or under the auspices of the WSDC. The National Association of Swing Dance Events (NASDE) also oversees routine competition, but it is a smaller organization; I think it only has twelve events. Even at independent comps, though, NASDE rules are generally followed for routines because the competitors doing those routines are usually also competing on the NASDE circuit.*

Hustle and Salsa

Disco America, held in Essington, Pennsylvania, is an annual event at which Hustle devotees convene for a weekend that includes opportunities to socialize, take lessons with well-known teachers and compete. I asked The Hustling Attorney, a.k.a. Erica Smith, to fill me in on competition in the Hustle and Salsa genres.

Me: *Are there central organizations in Hustle and Salsa that promote the dances, set the rules for competition, and keep track of points and rankings?*

Erica: *Yes. In Hustle, it's the International Hustle Dance Association [IHDA]. If you go to its website, you'll see it also maintains a calendar of sanctioned events. There is also information about the history of the dance and some instructional materials. In Salsa, it's the World Salsa Federation [WSF].*

Me: How do the comps go in Hustle and Salsa? Are they similar to West Coast in that there are Jack and Jills, heats people enter with a partner, and routines?

Erica: Hustle competition is very similar to West Coast competition. We have amateur competition, pro-am, and professional divisions. We have partnered heats – which we call Just Hustle – where you are dancing with a person you already know, but you don't know what the music will be. We also have Jack and Jills, where you enter as an individual and dance with people you don't know. We also have routines, and team formation competition. A team is made up of three or four couples that perform together, creating various patterns on the floor – a curving line, a diamond shape, whatever

Me: Oh, sort of like a drill team?

Erica: Yes. Teams can be made up of amateurs – those are called training teams – or made up of professionals. We also have something called bookends, which means two girls or two guys dancing together.

Me: Oh, really? Is that to accommodate gay folk?

Erica: Not necessarily. It's just same-sex. It doesn't have to be related to their sexuality.

Me: Wonderful! I love that! It bugs me that Ballroom defines a couple as a man and a woman. I'm also irked at being discouraged from learning to lead – although I'm doing it, anyway. Ballroom has very traditional roots.

Erica: We definitely don't have that problem in Hustle. In fact, just this year, we made changes to the IHDA which allow for same-sex competition throughout – in all divisions, not just in bookends.

Me: You mean in any form of competition, Just Hustle, Jack and Jill, Team and Routines, same-sex couples can dance alongside gender-mixed couples?

Erica: Right.

Me: Oh, Erica! If I didn't know I'd look ghastly in those skimpy dresses, I might switch to Hustle! Are there many women who can lead in Hustle? If so, why do they pursue that?

Erica: There are a lot of women who can lead in Hustle. Learning the opposite role helps you improve as a follow. If I'm leading as a female, I'm learning more about what leads need from follows. Also, it's challenging. It's challenging to lead in general, and challenging for a follow to learn the lead role. That's exciting for some people. Another reason is that a lot of times you'll go out dancing and there won't be enough leads, so if you can lead, you know you'll always be dancing the whole time.

Me: You're making my day here, Erica!

Erica: I have several students who both follow and lead.

Me: How about women who get asked to dance by another woman? Are they cool with that?

Erica: Yep. A lot of the time, they probably think to themselves, "This dance is going to be better than with a male lead, because she understands what it feels like to follow." As a woman, you're going to lead someone the way you like to be led.

Me: You mean not getting muscled around the floor and yanked around the turns?

Erica: Exactly! And, a lot of the guys are fine with being led by another guy. In our community, nobody gets a dirty look for dancing with a person of the same sex.

Me: Do many men who can lead decide to learn to follow?

Erica: I wouldn't say many, but there definitely are some.

Me: How about Salsa competition?

Erica: In Salsa, competition is mainly about routines. It also includes some strictlies and some team formation competition, but routines are by far the most popular.

Me: Do you wear pretty much the same thing in Salsa as in Hustle competition?

Erica: Yes. As you said, those skimpy dresses...and heels. In West Coast, I can get away with pants and flat shoes.

Me: *I know! I'm envious! Erica, I know West Coast events are not just about competition. There are workshops and private lessons available, as well as social dancing that goes on practically all night. Is that true of Hustle and Salsa comps, too?*

Erica: *Hustle and Salsa comps are definitely social events. Sometimes, both dances are done at the same comp and the event will be billed as Hustle/Salsa.*

Me: *How did you get to teach and judge? Did you have to earn any sort of credentials? I know the West Coast folks don't.*

Erica: *I didn't need any certifications or anything. It's pretty much the same. I competed as an amateur for several years and worked my way up through the competitive amateur ranks to the Advance Level. I was placing first or second in most of my events and it was suggested to me that I should think about turning pro. So, I started competing in professional divisions.*

Me: *Did you have to register anywhere to turn pro or go through any process?*

Erica: *I did have to register with the IHDA, but you're not required to belong to the Association in order to compete.*

Me: *What are the terms used to distinguish the levels of accomplishment in Hustle and Salsa?*

Erica: *In Hustle, we have pre-novice, novice, pre-intermediate, intermediate, advance, and all-star. In Salsa, it's bronze, silver, gold. I think there are levels beyond gold, too.*

Urban Dance

Tasha Barnes brought me up to speed about competition in Urban Dancing.

Me: Tasha, what are some of the major competitive events in Urban Dance?

Tasha: *Juste Debout, Battle of the Year, Funk In Stylez and Freestyle Sessions are big ones. Our [Urban Artistry] event, The International Soul Society Festival, held here in D.C., is growing in popularity. There are also jams – events where we just exchange [dance] together.*

Me: Can dancers compete in all the major styles at the same comp, or are there separate events for the various styles?

Tasha: *At most of the events we go to, there might be a Hip-Hop category and a House category, or there might be a Hip-Hop category and an All-Styles category, so everyone can get to perform the style of dance they like. The All-Styles category can mean all styles of music, or all styles of dance, depending on the comp. If "All-Styles" means music, you dance the style associated with the particular music being played – and you don't know ahead of time what that's going to be. If "All-Styles" means dance style, then you can dance whatever style you feel like dancing regardless of the music – both are awesome to watch!*

Me: At these comps, two people, or three, or four or however many will perform as a team, competing – I know you use the term battling – against other teams. Right?

Tasha: *Right. There are two-on-two battles, three-on-three, etc.*

Me: Can girls and guys be on the same team?

Tasha: *Yes. A team can be all guys, all girls, or mixed.*

Me: Is there any individual competition?

Tasha: Yes. In fact, our most popular form of competition is an individual form called the Seven-to-Smoke. The competitors will line up, and one – the King of the Hill – will dance, and then another one will dance, and those two are judged against each other. The one who wins that battle becomes King of the Hill and takes on the next person, and so forth, until someone wins seven of those match-ups and becomes the overall winner.

Me: Is Seven-to-Smoke a guy thing? If so, is there a similar female version?

Tasha: There is Seven-to-Smoke competition for women, too.

Me: Wow! S to S sounds intense…and exhausting. Do you have Jack and Jill competition?

Tasha: Yes, but we call them Bonnie and Clydes [laughs].They're more popular at B-Boy events. If there are not enough ladies, two guys will dance as a team. The team members perform separately and together.

Me: Tasha, you're a teacher and a judge. Did you have to get certified by an organization in order to teach and judge?

Tasha: No. Right now, there isn't an official certifying group. A dancer advances into the teaching and judging roles based on experience and knowledge gained and demonstrated over a number of years, and also by being battle-tested – succeeding in competition. A lot of us are also pursuing dance-related degrees in higher education. We're getting involved in the academia of Urban Dance.

Dancers who participate in competitions and showcases do so for a number of reasons having to do with personal growth, challenge and expression. Some extroverted types find competing comes naturally. Others, like Bonnie Stook, must find a strategy that allows them to be comfortable in the limelight:

Bonnie: *I'm no longer as afraid to be out there...to be seen... although at events, I still pretend I'm invisible – that people can't see me – so I can enjoy the actual dancing with my partner. I'm not a showman, but I really enjoy dancing. As long as I dance in my own world, I'm fine. If people enjoy watching, that's fine, too. But to me [whispers] I'm invisible. They can't see me, so I'm free to be me.*

I can relate to Bonnie's tactic of pretending she's not being observed, particularly when it comes to Latin dances such as Rumba and Bolero. I'm not a shy person, but I'm not exactly fresh from the prom, either. Getting my slinky on while dancing with a thirty-year-old takes a certain amount of nerve.

I have to know the crowd is behind me.

And it is.

Dina Daubenberger, who you will recall designs, rents and sells ballroom gowns, told me that for her, competition is about anticipation and personal challenge:

Dina: *It's something to look forward to. Something to work toward. If you're competing at a level that's new for you, you want to make sure when you get to the comp, you're ready to dance well at that level. So, it's personally challenging that way. It's like figure-skating. Those girls have practiced* *their routine a thousand times, but it's all about that one time they do it in front of those judges, on a different rink, all by themselves.*

It's like that in Ballroom. You've practiced your steps a million times in the studio, but when you get to the comp, things are going to be different. The size of the floor might be different. There's a lot of noise. There are other couples on the floor. You don't know what the music is going to be – and you're being judged. So all these things are thrown at you and you still need to dance well. So I think that is kind of exciting. You anticipate the comp. You look forward to it.

I think especially for women, the costumes are exciting. I mean what to wear is not a big deal for men, but for women, getting our outfits together is just SO fun. You don't wear things like that in your everyday life. You get a chance to wear something you would never wear in your real life – something people who know you would never imagine seeing you in. But at a comp, it's like you're allowed to have a different personality. You're supposed to be noticed. You're supposed to be loud. You want to be splashy. You have a ton of makeup on. Your hair is done – who doesn't like that?

And if you also dance well, it's such a feeling of accomplishment. And even if you don't do well, you're thinking, next time I want to do THIS. Or, next time, I'll improve on THAT. You're thinking ahead, because you know you'll get another chance. Like I said – for me, it's never about beating somebody else, or being the prettiest, or the thinnest or the best dancer, or any of that. It's none of that. It's about how I can be better next time. Even with respect to the costume...I can't tell you how many mistakes I've made with costumes. I would see the video and I would think, oh, my goodness, that wasn't what I'd intended. That didn't turn out the way I wanted it to. That helped me business-wise, too, because I didn't want to make the same mistake with someone else's costume.

Costumes and make-up and hair...oh my! While amongst avian species, it's the male bird that flaunts the gaudy plumage, in Ballroom, the opposite is true. Ladies strive for a larger-than-life look that will make it all but impossible for judges to overlook them on a crowded floor. Most sport a spray tan, an elaborate (but secure) hairdo, and heavy make-up calculated to exaggerate expression – an important component of artistry.

Competition, particularly on the professional level, combines intense physicality with elements of theater. Onlookers must be able to readily discern emotions dancers are attempting to convey – physically and facially.

Anton Marx wishes it was more widely understood that each dance is associated with a certain feeling:

Anton: Sometimes, when I watch people dance, I can see how much better they would look if they just moved their bodies in a way that conveyed emotion. For example, when women move away from their partner in Bolero, they should do it in a way that conveys reluctance. They need to show the woman does not really want to leave the man, but has to. The woman needs to move in a way that conveys that. And when she goes back to him, she does that with relish – and this calls for a different type of movement.

In International Standard and American Smooth heats, ladies wear long, flowing gowns embellished with rhinestones, crystals, beading, sequins, feathers, etc. Dancer Glenda Hingley, who dances in British Columbia with her husband, Bill, actually makes her own gowns...and they are GORGEOUS. Here's Glenda (dancing with Bill) in a stunning blue creation.

In International Latin and American Rhythm heats, those who can carry it off wear short, flashy, barely-there dresses intended to show off

what are known as *leg-lines*. The leg-line challenged usually wear something more forgiving. I, for example, am currently in the market for a heavily-beaded burka.

I also heard from several gentlemen on the subject of why they compete. John Grumbine, 97 years old, really enjoys dancing in showcase exhibitions and competitions:

John: *I've danced as many as 58 heats in two days. One time, in Las Vegas, I did a special routine in which I danced with two ladies at the same time. Another time, I did a routine in which I dressed like John Travolta. I had the white suit and the black shirt. It was fun! When I'm out there, I'm enjoying myself. But, I'm always wanting to do better, too. I think all dancers want to get better at it, no matter how good they are.*

Anton Marx also strives constantly for improvement:

Anton: *I don't know how other people feel, but I don't think I'll ever achieve the level of dance I want to. I have a visual ideal of how I want to look someday, and no matter how well I feel I've done at a competition, when I see the video, I don't like what I see.*

Don Youtz, whom you met in Chapter 2, dances at Top Hat Studio and competes in partnership with his wife Cheryl. Don likes the challenge of prepping for a comp:

Don: *I used to compete in sports when I was young. I love practicing for something. I love the challenge of learning something new. My goal is to do the best I can and not come in last. But if I don't place, no problem. I like the rush, the excitement, the butterflies before the event and then the gratification when it's over. To have that again when you're in your sixties is amazing. I particularly like the Jack and Jills where you dance a few songs with your own partner, and then you switch! You get judged on how you dance with your own partner and the new one.*

Dancers who are serious about competition put a lot of time into improving their dancing:

Anton: *We dance six days a week at our studio. They're closed on Sunday. Otherwise, we'd be there then, too. We each take an individual lesson, plus another one as a couple, every week, plus all the group lessons.*

Dance events are not just about strutting one's stuff and measuring oneself against others; they are about reconnecting with the larger tribe – people from other studios you may not have seen for a while – scoping out the gorgeous costumes, and cheering people on. The social dance industry is about teaching a skill, yes, but it's also about making sure people are enjoying themselves. Pretty much every staff member working at showcase or a competition – from the announcer to the music guy to the judges – is loaded with personality and charisma. There is always a certain amount of goofy hacking around, too.

Is competition for you? Perhaps not. Many dancers never compete. While your studio will try to entice you (the comp scene is a source of revenue) you won't be made to feel like a second-class citizen if you decline.

On the other hand, maybe you'll look better in sequins than you think!

14

Dancing is for Everyone:

Why All Your Excuses are Bogus!

Life begins at the end of your comfort zone. ~Neale Donald Walsch

As a self-appointed Ambassador of Ballroom (and other genres) who constantly extols partner dancing's benefits and attempts to cajole people into studios and clubs, I've heard just about every possible excuse for not giving dancing a try: *I don't have a partner*; *I can't keep time*; *I'm too fat*; *I'm too old*; *I can't afford it*; *I'm black, brown, gay, or handicapped*; *dancing isn't manly.* I seldom buy these excuses, because in most instances, they just don't hold water. Allow me to refute them.

I DON'T HAVE A PARTNER

You don't need a partner. If you're a guy (known, at least in the Ballroom world, as a *gentleman*), you will be free to invite both escorted and unescorted ladies onto the floor. Studios and clubs encourage dancers to mix it up – dance with different partners – for two reasons: dancing with one person can get boring, and dancing with a variety of people sharpens dancers' skills, "leads" and "follows" alike.

Fellas, don't be afraid to invite ladies who are a bit ahead of you, skill-wise, to dance. Trust me, we all want to be up and moving, and some of us will be hesitant to ask *you* – although really, every day is Sadie Hawkins Day at most venues. A lady not particularly challenged by your steps can work on her posture, motion, footwork, arm-styling, etc. Bottom line: we'd rather be dancing with *you* than sitting down.

Here are the facts of the matter for unescorted *ladies*. At Ballroom-oriented studios and clubs, couples slightly outnumber singles, and among singles, women outnumber men. The opposite is true in studios/clubs that focus on dances such as Swing and Hustle: single attendees outnumber couples and men are as well-represented as women. Regardless of the venue she chooses, however, once a lady starts taking lessons – particularly group lessons – and attending parties, she will start to get to know people. Eventually, she will integrate into the community and both attached and single gentlemen will ask her to dance. If the studio provides instructors at parties, she won't even have to endure an *I'm a stranger in these parts* period because teachers will dance with her from day one.

Here's what Jameson Kilburn has to say on the subject of ladies asking gentlemen to dance:

Jameson: I get frustrated when women wait around for someone to ask them. I think all dancers, especially in the lower levels, are insecure. The stress of having to put themselves up for rejection shouldn't be put on just one gender. So we here at the studio strongly foster that anyone can ask anyone to dance at any time. We also have a lot of women who lead. They come to group classes to learn the leader role. We've always been very gender blind in terms of dancing. Some men prefer to follow and some women prefer to lead. In the Hustle, Salsa and West Coast Swing communities, it's not uncommon for women to lead. In ballroom dances such as Waltz, it's less common. In the class I just taught last Tuesday, I had three women leading and two men following. It takes people a little while to get used to seeing that when

they first come in, but they soon fall right into it and it becomes more about the dance than anything else.

I CAN'T KEEP TIME

Well, maybe you can't right now, but chances are, you can learn.

Don Youtz was not a natural at hearing the rhythms in music:

Don: *When I started, I couldn't find the beat. It was a good six months maybe a year, before I became confident. It was very frustrating. Now, it's amazing, but I can pick out the beat in any song.*

According to Oliver Sack's book *Musicophilia*, true *rhythm deafness*, the inability to perceive the beat in a piece of music, is quite rare. The very few people who do have it are either born with it or develop it subsequent to a stroke. According to neurological researcher Jessica Phillips-Silver, the ability to perceive cadence exists apart from hearing.[81] Even people who are profoundly deaf can perceive and keep time to a beat, providing they can feel it in their bodies or watch someone else clapping or otherwise moving to it. In general, if you can clap your hands in time to music, you're not rhythm deaf. Most people who think they can't keep time to music are incorrect. What they are

---

[81] Nierenburg, C. (March 15th, 2014). Can't feel the rhythm? You may be "beat deaf." NBC News. Downloaded from http://www.nbcnews.com/health/body-odd/cant-feel-rhythm-you-may-be-beat-deaf-f1C6437334.

actually having trouble with is coordinating their physical movements with the rhythm.

The ease with which we detect a given rhythm is related to our cultural experience. At six months of age, infants can readily detect all rhythmic variations, but as one-year olds, they have a narrower range and detect most easily the types of rhythms to which they've been exposed. By adulthood, most peoples' rhythmic range has narrowed still further and it may be hard to find the beat in "foreign" music.

The bottom line? Only very "special" people are not physically equipped to learn to keep time. Chances are, you're not special!

I'M NOT WELL-COORDINATED

Glad to hear it! That's an absolutely excellent reason to take up dancin'! As we get older, many adults abandon the sports we enjoyed in our youth, and consequently lose ground in terms of balance, agility, flexibility, and all-around gracefulness. Remember the Chapter 2 info about the body benefits of boogie? If you give it a chance, you will be amazed at how rapidly your nervous system will respond to dancing's demands.

I'M TOO FAT

No, you're not. If you can walk, you can dance – and if you're overweight, you *need* to. Plus, heavy people can be really good dancers, as instructor Jameson Kilburn points out:

Jameson: John Lindo, from New Jersey, is a champion West Coast Swing dancer and a very large man. He towers over me by at least a foot and I couldn't reach my arms around him if I tried. And, he's one of the most celebrated dancers in his genre. People nicknamed him Jungle Gym because he can do tricks with the girls most guys just can't manage. Instead of changing his body, he chose to embrace it, and it's now part of what makes him so wonderfully who he is – I couldn't imagine him being any other way. That's what I meant when I said it's not always about changing who we are. It's about looking...and then asking, "Do I like this?" And if it's a "Yes," celebrate it. If it's a "No," change it.

Curious about that Lindo fella? I was too. Watch the video of him competing in a *Jack and Jill* (footnoted below). To really appreciate his moves, recall that *Jack and Jill* means both partners are dancing with a randomly-selected participant to music of which they had no advance knowledge.

Jungle Jim is not the only heavy person who can float like a feather on the floor. Stefanie Lein, the Arizona dancer who enlightened us about the intricacies of Ballroom judging in Chapter 13, chronicles her struggles with weight and dancing in her popular blog, *Biggest Girl In the Ballroom*. Stef may be a woman of size, but, as you can tell from the footnoted video of her uncorking a sizzling Cha Cha routine with instructor, Ivan Dishliev – the lady can dance![82]

---

[82] Watch the Stef/Ivan video at: http://youtu.be/JTYLVPC2Aog

If finding out you're perfectly capable of learning to dance came as a surprise, here's more good news: overweight people are not stigmatized in dance studios.

To be stigmatized is to be perceived by others as having a characteristic that sets you apart from them. Obesity, along with various types of disabilities and deformities, can constitute a *physical* stigma. Amanda Spahr, a very large lady, told me how much being accepted by her dance community means to her:

Amanda: When I initially went to take lessons before my wedding, I remember feeling afraid because I'm 200 pounds overweight, and I thought, "People are really going to judge me...I'm going to get in there and people are going to think, OMG, I have to dance with this lady...she's so fat she shouldn't be here." I had all these negative thoughts in my head, and when I walked in the door, I was thinking I would wind up leaving early...feeling traumatized and judged. Of course, the exact opposite happened...the studio is the one place I don't feel judged for my weight. Once in a while, I'll feel a new student judging me, but most of the time, from the teachers and students who know me, I don't feel that.

Some people – mostly those who've been slim all their lives – think being overweight or obese is entirely voluntary. They think weakness of will or lack of pride in one's appearance are the only factors involved.

Having fought fat for most of my life, I know better.

I know most overweight people are far from unconcerned about their excess poundage.

I know most have battled it valiantly – as I did – only to find themselves defeated repeatedly by a stronger adversary.

While a few bravely demand an end – not to their fatness but the persecution to which they are subjected – I think most heavy people would be thin if they could. I consider myself extraordinarily lucky to have stumbled onto the passion, or the community – or both – that somehow saved me from myself. I bless the day that Arthur Murray Groupon showed up in my inbox.

If it hadn't, I'm pretty sure I'd still be fat.

I have, however, asked myself why the Arthur Murray Miracle has not been visited upon *all* my studio mates. Why are some who've been dancing for years still a little on the plump side? While there is likely no definitive answer that fits all cases, I've come across some factors that may be relevant.

Some people simply burn calories more readily than others.

I once had a friend who consistently ate *much* more than I did and never gained a pound over the years I knew her. She didn't work out, either. Perhaps some of the svelte dancers may have been gifted with a metabolism such as my friend's – one that burns an unusually large number of calories in an average day without deliberate exercise.

That metabolic rates can indeed differ dramatically has been scientifically verified. In one study, two individuals with the same bodily ratio of fat-to-lean tissue were found to have astonishingly different metabolisms.[83] One burned 715 more calories/per day *at rest* than the other. Moreover, in a study developed for the BBC documentary "Why Do Some People Never Get Fat?" Dr. Carel LeRoux found that some lucky people seem to put on *muscle*, rather than fat, when they scarf down more calories than their bodies need.

Unfair? You betcha.

It's even possible your provenance has something to do with your genetic profile.

Pathway Labs, in San Diego, markets a genetic test predicated on the assumption that some foods are especially "fattening" for people

---

[83] Speakman, J. R. (2005). Body size, energy metabolism and lifespan. *Journal of Experimental Biology*, 208.

with certain genomic characteristics – that consuming foods to which we are genetically ill-suited causes the body to store excess fat.

While there are several theoretical variations on this theme, the central assumption is that the part of the world (cold, hot, suited/unsuited to agriculture, etc.) determined the foods our remote ancestors ate – and the foods our bodies process most efficiently today. That assumption is controversial, given the mixed ancestry most of us have, but perhaps definitive supporting evidence will be found.

Genetics aside, I suspect food preferences have a lot to do with how many chins we have.

For most of my life, I've been burdened by what I call *fat druthers* – I'd druther have a donut than a salad. Yet, I have friends (am I tolerant, or what?) who absolutely *love* salads, and veggies in general, and eat them out of *preference* – as opposed to Spartan discipline. Perhaps some of the more streamlined dancers are in the latter category.

Or, perhaps those who succeeded in losing weight after taking up dancing succeeded in changing their tastes, as I did. While I still have to be very careful around sweets, my overall food preferences are now much more thin-friendly than they were. Going without heavy food for a year relieved me of my desire for it. I no longer even *want* to eat the heavy, cheese-laden entrées available at many popular restaurants.

I suspect motivation is another key factor in determining whether dancing will influence weight loss. As I've said, I was raised in a fat-phobic family – I remember well the day my mother looked at my sturdy, pre-teen thighs and said, "When I was your age, I was a LOT better-looking."

Yes, the woman was ill.

But from that day, being even slightly overweight became unacceptable to me. Thank God I found dancing and can now, in Daphne Rose Kingma's beautiful words… "reside in my body in peace."

Happily, not all families are as fat-biased as mine. It's possible – though, I suspect, uncommon – to have a large body and feel not only unashamed but *attractive*. And of course, not every *zaftig* person gets a health scare the way Harvey, the former naval officer you met in Chapter 2, did.

Finally, there is even some evidence that in comparison with being underweight, being slightly overweight (not obese) may be healthier.[84]

I'M TOO OLD

If you think you're too old to dance, John Grumbine and Tish Dame beg to differ.

John – the 97-year-old who was born in a log cabin – started taking lessons at Arthur Murray York, Pennsylvania, when he was 84, after the death of his first wife. John recently lost his second wife, Betsy (whom he met at a dance), but still takes lessons, attends studio parties and performs at showcases. He memorizes complicated ballroom routines choreographed by his teacher, Kristin Rude, and dances them with her during events. John's fitness routine includes not only dancing several times a week, but doing five miles a day on his exercise bike.

John: *I mentally run through my dance steps in my mind while I'm riding. I feel sorry when I see people younger than I am who are having difficulty mentally and physically. I think I'm doing the right things for myself...dancing to me is a way of making a joyful expression of your life...I wouldn't trade my dancing experience for two million dollars.*

---

[84] Bacon, L. (2008). Health at any size: the surprising truth about your weight. Dallas, Tx: BenBella Books.

Tish Dame, 87 years old and the self-described "oldest dame in the studio" has been dancing at Arthur Murray Lemoyne, Pennsylvania for the past six years. Tish, pictured with her friend Pete Camasi, started dancing when she was 81, subsequent to having been widowed after a long marriage:

Tish: *My husband was in the Navy. We were married almost 58 years. He passed away of leukemia ten years ago, and I got really depressed. I didn't do anything for five years. Then one day, I was driving past the studio and I thought, "I'll go in and see what they say." I had taken some lessons at an Arthur Murray back in 1974 and liked it. So I went in, and an instructor who was there at the time, Carlos, started right in with the Tango, and I just loved it! And of course, I'm still there! It's lovely. You feel like family. Dancing is all I ever do. I don't go to movies or anything. I just go dancing. It gets me out of the house, and makes me energetic. I'm just so much happier since I started dancing. I don't want to stop! It makes me feel wonderful. If I stayed home all the time, I'd feel depressed. I live with my daughter and son-in-law and they work all day. The exercise is good for me, too. My doctor says, "Keep doing what you're doing." And I know having to remember all the steps is good for my brain.*

Tish and Pete, from whom you heard in Chapter 6, dance in most of the competitions their studio holds or attends:

Me: *Tish, why do you go to the comps? In what way is that meaningful to you?*

Tish: I guess I like to show off! [laughs]. I don't really mean that, but it is fun! At the last one, I did 46 heats and I got Gold in every one of them. I like going to different places. The people from Severna Park [an Arthur Murray studio in Maryland] are so nice. And two of the instructors from there, Alon [Pilcher] and Paul [Pietrzak] always dance with me. They give me a big hug, too. They're so sweet!

Me: You did 46 heats?! I only did 32 and I was pooped! It's just fantastic you can do that many.

Tish: Well, I was kind of wearing out, but I love it! It keeps me going.

Me: Do you dance anywhere other than studio events?

Tish: Sometimes we go down to Mount Holly Springs. They have a band and a dance floor, and a nice buffet.

According to a study done in 2002, senior dancers like John and Tish dance not only because they enjoy it, but because they see it as a way of refuting the *old = physically infirm* stereotype.[85] Dancing is a particularly appropriate form of physical activity for older people because it can be modified as time passes. Dancers can choose relatively more or less vigorous styles and rhythms according to their capability. The study also revealed that the social network dancing provides is an important source of support for older people during major life events such as bereavement.

Joints getting creaky? Dancing could help. In one study,[86] nursing home residents with hip and knee pain required almost 40% less medication, and were able to walk faster, after dancing twice a week for only twelve weeks. Maintaining our ability to walk at a decent clip as we get older is important. We have to be able to cross streets safely by ourselves – and make it to the bathroom before something unfortunate happens – if we want to maintain our independence.

---

[85] Thomas, H., Cooper, L. (2002). Dancing into the third age: social dance as cultural text, 20(1).
[86] Krampe, J., Wagner, J. et al. (2014). Does dance-based therapy increase gait speed in adults with chronic joint pain: a feasibility study. Geriatric Nursing. In press.

The broad age-range typically found at dance studios benefits older and younger people alike. For example, it has helped Amanda Spahr feel more comfortable with older people:

Amanda: *Another way in which dance has helped me socially is that I used to be uncomfortable talking to older people, but I've met a lot of them at Arthur Murray and now I really enjoy talking to them. Some of the people who support me the most are much older than I am.*

Wait…I'm not done with you yet.

Fair warning, this next bit is going to sound weird.

If you place yourself in an atmosphere that reminds you of your youth, it's possible you will actually *become* younger, at least in terms of biological age markers such as mobility and eyesight, etc.

In what is known as the *Counter-Clockwise Study*, Harvard psychologist Ellen Langer (www.ellenlanger.com) arranged for a group of volunteers in their 70s and 80s to reside for a week in a home that had been turned into a sort of time-capsule that went back twenty years. The clothing, décor, furnishings, kitchen appliances, general reading material, newspapers, music and cuisine recreated, as closely as possible, the environment the volunteers had experienced when they were two decades younger. Langer's subjects were instructed to refer to themselves and their families as they had been during that period, and to refrain from discussing contemporary events.

The study's results are simply jaw-dropping.

Hearing, visual acuity, memory, manual dexterity and appetite improved in *all* subjects. Volunteers who had been using canes at the beginning of the study walked unaided by the end of it. No changes occurred in the similarly-aged control group, which had resided for a week in a contemporary environment.

The Counter-Clockwise Study's results illustrate the mind's profound effect on the body. Helen Langer believes it is this *mind-body effect* that causes some people in their 70s or 80s to act and appear old, while others don't. How people think about themselves (self-concept, self-talk and expectations) is reflected in their physicality. If we see ourselves as worn down and worn out, our bodies will prove us right.

Here's a bit of relevant wisdom from Jon Acuff's wonderful book, *Start*:

> *Age is no longer the primary factor that determines where you are on the map. Life is now less about how old you are and more about when you decide to live.... Regardless of your age or station in life, it all comes down to one simple truth: you just have to start.*

We must mind the "marching orders" our minds give our bodies. Whether the destination turns out to be a relatively healthy, zestful third season – or an early grave – is at least partly up to us.

Changed your mind about being too old to start dancin'? Inspire yourself further by checking out www.ballroomsparkle.com. Along with pictures of the stunning dresses she designs and sells, Maria Chitul posts wonderful essays on choosing dresses that flatter mature women, and dresses that camouflage limitations such as a slouched spine, weak hip motion, an overabundance of booty, etc.

I'M BLACK OR BROWN

Unfortunately, among the still quite robust population of unenlightened souls in this country, darker skin tones are still considered stigmatizing.

Stigma based on race, nationality or religion, is referred to as *tribal* stigma and happily, it seems to be as irrelevant as other forms of stigma at dance studios. At Arthur Murray York, Lancaster and Lemoyne, Pennsylvania, for example, people of Indian, Puerto Rican, Chinese and African-American descent are sprinkled among the Caucasian majority and I've never heard or seen anyone express the slightest hesitation about dancing with one of them, nor has the subject ever come up during an interview. One racially-mixed (Caucasian-Black) couple even played up their external difference at an event – a showcase, I think. They did a routine – a choreographed exhibition performance during which they were the only couple on the floor – and wore, respectively, black and white outfits that heightened their natural contrast. I asked Earle David Reed, who constitutes one-half of said couple, about his experience as an African-American dancer:

Earle: *I've never felt uncomfortable about race at the studio. Just in general, I can't be concerned about that because who I am is not going to change. I think a better question is, do they feel uncomfortable with me? If anyone were to come up to me and say something really stupid or silly – that's on them. If I let that bother me, I'd never leave the house. So I just try to be the best me that I can.*

I know when some people see me, they think, oh, he probably does this or that, but I think that being honest and accomplished and successful helps alleviate that. I've never had the feeling that someone didn't want to dance with me. Even back in the '50s when people would get beaten up for dancing together, it was never about those people themselves. It was about the people around them. Music is one of those things that bring people together. Even back in the day when black and white people would have to dance in separate sections of a club or whatever, they'd still all be there – the music brought them together.

Carline Coleman was a bit worried about race when she first found herself at her studio.

Carline: *Dancing lets me meet people, and have fun. At places like the Sheraton [where a recent event was held] I get to wear beautiful ball gowns and have a lovely, formal dinner. And you meet all kinds of people – all ages and ethnic groups – and everybody gets along. It's like we have our own little community. Dancers understand one another. At first I was a little bit afraid of it. I was worried about being African-American, but I feel very much at home.*

I'M GAY

If you're lesbian, gay, bisexual or transgender (LGBT), I've got good news for you! Dancing is an arty endeavor and art communities are particularly accepting of people who deviate from the so-called heterosexual norm. There have been gay and lesbian couples at my studio – no "out" singles of whom I'm aware – and they have been well-received. Other students displayed no reluctance to dance with them, and during group classes, the instructors were good about using the terms *leads* and *follows* in lieu of *ladies* and *gentlemen,* which is customary in Ballroom, but much less so in other genres.

Nevertheless, the studio has not been successful at retaining its same-sex couples for significant periods of time. Over the past three years or so, I've encountered several who stayed for only a while: a male couple who were prepping for their wedding and did not continue afterward, and two female couples that eventually drifted away.

Happily, I found one studio at which a pair of ladies – very interesting ladies – had settled in nicely.

I'd been looking for gay interviewees and when I was referred to Emily Baker and her legal spouse MaryAnn Primo, I assumed they fit the bill – until Emily shared that she is transgender, not gay, and described MaryAnn as heterosexual:

Emily: *Contrary to any outside appearances, I am a male with a very small feminine side. Had medicine been more advanced I would be 100% male today. Maybe the next few generations will have more choices. But, I decided many years ago to not have any surgical processes and to live my life with a partner who was essentially a "straight" woman. Ironically, we are not a gay couple, but that concept is damned near impossible for most people to understand. Same-sex is also not really an accurate term either, beyond the physical aspects.*

Emily is a person coping with *gender dysphoria* – a strong, consistent feeling of identification with the opposite gender, together with discomfort with one's own biological sex.[87] In short, Emily feels she is a male person trapped in a female body. Emily explained to me how fulfilling dancing the leader role can be:

Emily: *So imagine my surprise when we entered the world of dance and I was instantly able and expected to "BE" the male. It has challenged and rewarded the very core of who I am and has stripped away that protective layer that I have so successfully built to protect myself from the world. Being "two spirited" [a Native-American concept] in the gay world is not much different than the straight world. I don't fit in either and so the wall of personal protection is the same, with different characteristics for the audience.*

The physical challenges [of dancing] have been pure fun for me. This is the first time in my 45 years that I have been encouraged and

---

[87] PsychCentral staff (2014). Gender dysphoria. Downloaded from http://psychcentral .com/disorders/gender-dysphoria-symptoms.

expected to thrive as my REAL SELF in something that is part of the real world. Dance is clear cut and the rules are precise. There is one follower and one leader, and that brings a world of total clarity for me. Even now it is a difficult concept to describe.

While Emily and MaryAnn seem content at their studio, I wish more LGBT folk would join them. Being the sole representatives of a minority group (in *any* setting) must have its difficulties.

If you are gay, lesbian, bi-sexual, transgender – or define yourself as other than a heterosexual male or female – you may wish to check out the North American Same-Sex Partner Dance Association at http://www.nasspda.org/home/.

I'M DISABLED/HANDICAPPED

If you have a disability or handicap, you may well be physically capable of dancing, even if you think you're not.

One of the dancers at my studio is blind.

Kim Szcypta, a former data analyst who has been dancing for over four years, was born blind in her right eye. She lost her sight completely about a year prior to this interview, after sustaining damage to her left eye. Dancing was very important to Kim before she lost her sight. Now, it's even more so.

Kim: Right now, dancing is the only thing in my life I have control over. When you lose your sight, you really lose everything. I'm a blind person living in a sighted world. Being that I was sighted for so many years, blindness is a major change. I can get around my house because I know where everything is, but I can't go outside unaccompanied right now. They tell me maybe later I'll be able to go out alone – maybe even back to

work – but right now, I leave the house only to go grocery shopping with my husband, to the occasional doctor's appointment, and to the studio.

My eye doctor, whose mother is a dance instructor, told me there was no reason to give up dancing. He said, "You don't need your sight to dance. You follow, so you don't need to see." He was right – I don't. As long as my partner has hold of one of my hands so I know where he is, I'm good. And I'm so glad, because dancing is my life-saver. It's the only thing I can do.

Me: *How did the studio staff respond when you showed up completely blind?*

Kim: *Actually, they've been very good about it – very, very good about it. It's made them stop and think, because when I go to group class, they have to figure out how they're going to teach a move without me being able to see it. The teachers usually say, "Watch what I do." Well, I can't watch what they do, so they've had to develop other methods.*

Me: *Such as?*

Kim: *Tim [T.H.] keeps coming up with analogies…things to say that help me figure out what he's trying to teach me. For example, he once told me I needed to "make a backwards U-turn," and I understood what he meant. If the instructors can't come up with an analogy, they'll walk me through what they want me to do. Or, they might physically arrange my feet the way they want them to be, so that I get the idea. It's all working very well. Tim just taught me two new dances – Bolero and Two-Step – that I'm going to do at Showcase [an upcoming dance exhibition]. I've never done either one of them before. Tim and I are excited about it.*

Me: *Whoa! I'm gob-smacked that you've not only been able to learn two new and difficult dances, but that you are up for all the stress and hubbub associated with competition, too.*

Kim: *If it wouldn't be for Tim, I wouldn't be going to Showcase. He said to me, "You gotta show off the way you dance now, because you dance so much better than you did when you had your vision."*

Me: *You're blowing my mind, here. You dance better?*

Kim: *It's because I can follow better now that I've lost my sight. Most women have a tendency to anticipate the lead and get a little ahead of it, especially if they know the pattern.*

Me: *Oh, yeah. I've had that pointed out to me. (About a million times).*

Kim: *But since all I can do is feel what the leader is doing, I've learned to be very, very responsive to his slightest movement. Ron [Ron Christy, a visiting coach] was amazed when he saw me dancing with Justin [Howard] one day. He said, "You've lost all anticipation; you've lost all hesitation – you just go with the flow." Another time, I was dancing Viennese Waltz [a very fast dance that involves constant rotation] with Urs [judge/coach Urs Geisenhainer], and he was amazed at how much my dancing has improved since I went blind.*

Me: *You do Viennese?! With all that whirling and twirling? Don't you get dizzy?*

Kim: *It depends on how I'm holding my head. If it's in the right position, I don't get dizzy. I can do spins in Swing, too. Tim knows that if I squeeze his arm with my left hand, it means I'm getting dizzy and he'll switch to a different move that gives me time to collect my bearings. When I loosen my grip, he knows I'm OK again.*

Me: *It's amazing what you've accomplished, considering.*

Kim: *I just did my 60% bronze III checkout and Lynn [studio owner Lynn Reigle] said, "You know, we do have a handicapped program," and Tim said, "I don't think Kim wants you to consider her handicapped." He was right. I don't consider myself handicapped. I consider myself blind, not handicapped.*

Me: *How have the students at your studio reacted to your blindness?*

Kim: *Some have been wonderful – kind, considerate and caring. For example, they will make sure that I get around the studio safely. Back to my seat after a group lesson, for example. Or they help me get a shoe buckled. And they'll come over to me and say, "Hello, how are you?" like they always did. But, there are others who don't even acknowledge me anymore. They've known me all this time, and all of a sudden,* *they're very stand-offish. That pisses me off. What's the difference between then and now? What does it matter that I can't see them?*

But, I've found out that's going to happen everywhere I go. There are people in this world that once they hear that word, handicapped, boom! They don't want anything to do with you. I'm scared to death of Showcase, because I know I'll get attitude there, too. I wish people would just treat me like they normally would.

Kim went to Showcase and danced well. She and Pete Camasi – who'd returned to competition after surviving a serious heart attack – were given special *Guts and Glory* awards by the studio.

Like obesity, physical disability is classified as a trait-related stigma. That's something Pete Camasi understands all too well.

Pete has *tardive dyskinesia* (T.D.), a neuromuscular condition that causes repetitive, involuntary body movements. Pete's shoulders and arms writhe uncontrollably during his waking hours and he has endured this condition for most of his life. He was afflicted with T.D. at the age of 16 – a reaction, his doctors said, to medication. Nonetheless, Pete is able to dance, and has been doing so at Arthur Murray Lemoyne, Pennsylvania, for quite a number of years.

Pete: All my life I'd shied away from events that involve dancing because I didn't know how and because of the movement disorder, although I'd always wanted to learn. I decided to take dance lessons because my daughter asked me to do it for her wedding. That was something I would have done anything for. Dancing has really helped my legs – my strength and my balance. Rumba is my favorite. It's kind of a jerky dance

to begin with and that suits me perfectly.

Sometimes I have problems with dances that are too fast, because the information from my brain about what my legs are supposed to do gets transmitted too slowly. By the time my legs respond, it's too late and I'm off the beat.

My second favorite is Hustle. It's one of the fast dances I can do. I'm also starting to get into Tango.

While Pete feels like a valued member of his dance community, he is aware the spasmodic movement in his arms puts some ladies off:

Pete: *Sometimes in a group class, I've noticed that some women would rather not dance with me. They'll actually physically get out of line to avoid dancing with me. It gets to me, but I just have to learn to accept that. One woman made the comment, "It's always an experience dancing with you." I wasn't sure what she meant by that.*

If you have a disability, don't just assume you can't dance. Tim Greene, a seasoned instructor who has been teaching Ballroom for Arthur Murray Central Pennsylvania, has seen disabled people not only cope well with dancing but improve their level of function:

Tim Greene: *I remember a couple who danced together and loved it – until the husband had a serious stroke which made it impossible for him to dance. I kept in touch with them and invited them to the [studio] holiday dinner, and they came back for that. The husband was in a wheel chair and had paralysis on his right side. His speech was hard to understand. At one point, he signaled that he wanted to stand up...so we helped*

him do that, and he embraced his wife in a dance frame and just held her as best he could, and they just swayed... because he wanted to dance with her so much.

His wife told me that after the stroke, the first word he had said in the hospital was "dance," because he was worried he'd never be able to do that again. And gradually, he got a little better, and would come into the studio on a cane. His wife said the rehab people had been amazed at the progress he'd made. They chalked it up to his determination to get back to dancing, which he eventually did. He was doing really well until unfortunately, money got tight and they had to stop dancing. I hated to see that because it was doing him so much good. I wish there was a way to convince insurance companies that dancing is good therapy, because it is. I've seen that, over and over.

More recently, a lady with a history of childhood polio came into the studio wearing leg braces. As she continued to dance, her mobility improved and she graduated to crutches. She amazed me with what she could do. She wanted to be challenged...and most of the time, she wound up doing what she made up her mind to do. I'm glad she told me she wanted to be challenged because I might have been afraid to push her. She was an inspiration.

Remember Elizabeth Metzger, the social worker who drives 70 miles to her studio and another 70 back? She, too, dances in spite of having significant physical limitations:

Elizabeth: *I have a chronic illness, a connective tissue disorder called Ehlers-Danlos Syndrome. Because of that, I have a certain level of joint and muscle pain most of the time, and I naturally dislocate my joints if I'm not very careful. The teachers, particularly my main*

teacher, Justin [Howard] have been great about helping me find ways to dance safely in spite of my illness. Lynn [Reigle – owner of the Lemoyne, York and Lancaster, Pennsylvania franchises] has helped me work on my balance, which was a big issue. She's helped me to learn to move on my own without feeling that I'm going to fall if I don't lean on my partner. Karly [Heck] has helped me with arm movements. I need to protect my shoulder during turns so I don't dislocate it. She's helped me come up with different movements during Peek-a-Boo [a pattern in which the arm and hand are usually thrust upward], too, so I don't get hurt. Chris [Lindy] pushes me – not farther than I can actually go, but he often makes me do more than I thought I could. They all know I don't want to be babied. I made that clear. All the teachers have helped me. They all offer something a little bit different.

Kim, Pete and Elizabeth are living (and dancing) proof that skating legend Scott Hamilton was absolutely right on when he said, *"The only disability in life is a bad attitude."*

Perhaps the most moving I-can-dance-anyway story is that of Arienne Haslet, a young instructor at the Arthur Murray studio in Boston, Massachusetts, who lost part of her left leg in the 2013 Boston Marathon bombings. About a year after the tragedy, Arienne danced the Rumba (with partner Christian Lightner) before an enthralled audience at a T.E.D. conference in Vancouver.[88]

---

[88] Watch the Arienne and Christian video at: http://youtu.be/ZQVO6Wi_7c8

The degree of disability dancing can accommodate is amazing. Amy Purdy, a recent competitor on *Dancing with the Stars*, is a double lower-limb amputee and danced astoundingly well on the show.[89]

The International Dance Federation (IDF), a non-profit organization that aims to promote dance throughout the world, has classes and events specifically geared toward dancers who are coping with various disabilities. The American Dance Wheels Foundation (ADWF) serves wheelchair-bound dancers. Don't miss the lovely footnoted video, *Randy and Diane's Waltz*, from the ADWF website.[90]

[89] Watch the Amy Purdy video at: http://youtu.be/Ckoimo7amdE
[90] Watch the *Randy and Diane's Waltz* video at: http://americandancewheels.org/gallery/videos.shtml

DANCING ISN'T MANLY

This one really bugs me because it's the *nee plus ultra* of bogus and it holds too many men back from a pasttime that could enrich their lives.

Straight guys: Listen up! I get it that you're scared to death of doing anything even remotely associated with the feminine because somebody might assume you're…GASP!… *gay*. Society attached that particular set of puppet strings to you early, and you're still getting jerked around by them. But put your thinking caps on for a minute. Were Fred Astaire, Arthur Murray and Gene Kelly gay? Not as far as I know. How about John Travolta and Patrick Swayze? No, again. Oh, and let's not forget Maks Chmerkovsky, the resident stud on *DWTS* – anything effeminate about him?

Are some of the males in the dance world gay? Of course. But, *some* is not the same as *most*. While it is true that some disciplines within dance seem to attract more gay guys than others – researchers estimate the percentage of gay or bisexual men among ballet and theater dancers to be just over 50 percent[91] – there is *no* evidence that those statistics apply to partner dance.

If you show up at a social dance studio – provided it's not located on Fire Island – you absolutely will *not* find yourself surrounded by flamboyantly homosexual men. Most of the guy pros (instructors and coaches) I've met are married to women. None – with one exception, now that I think about it – exhibits any stereotypically gay characteristics. As for male students, they are overwhelmingly married or looking to meet girls. As I mentioned in the previous section, I wish more gay folk of both genders felt free to dance alongside straights in public.

Wanting to dance, learning to dance and becoming a good dancer will in no way impugn your masculinity. For gosh' sake, guys, some of you fought in wars! Don't you think you've earned the right to follow your bliss onto the dance floor, if that's where it takes you?

---

[91] Carmen, J. (2006). Gay men in dance. Dance Magazine. Downloaded from http://www.dancemagazine.com/issues/November-2006/Gay-Men--Dance

Remember those puppet strings I mentioned earlier? Earle David Reed's were firmly in place when he first got interested in Ballroom, but he yanked 'em off, PDQ:

Earle: Even though I wanted to do it, at first I was worried it wasn't very masculine. I thought, 'What guy wants to do that?' But then I got into the studio and I saw the male instructors and I was like, 'Oh, I wanna be like them!' There is nothing effeminate about it. Here's what I learned as I got older: the sooner you decide you don't have to be cool, life gets so much easier and your mind opens up. It's a shame that youth has to be wasted on young people. Dancing is a challenge. You can keep getting better and better. You're never done improving yourself. It's given me confidence.

If you're at a function where there's dancing...a wedding or whatever, you can handle yourself. You're not out there flopping around. Most people at outside functions simply cannot dance the way we [trained dancers] do...you have to deliberately learn to do that. It's that whole Superman concept. When he was on Krypton, he was nothing special, but here on Earth – Wow! It's the same thing with dancing. At the studio, among other dancers, you might be nothing special, but outside the studio, on your worst day, you look better than pretty much anybody else.

I suspect many men would love to try dancing, if they weren't afraid of being judged. I heard about one crafty fellow who managed to get himself into a studio while making it seem like his wife's idea:

Cherella: When we first signed up at the studio, they asked us which dances we wanted to learn and I was shocked when I saw Anton circle Samba and a lot of other dances. I hadn't known he wanted to learn that. I hadn't even known he wanted to dance at all! He'd gotten the lessons as a birthday present for me. Or so I thought.

The idea that dancing is inconsistent with masculinity is just nuts.

Pro dancers are graceful, yes, but they are also strong, quick and incredibly fit. Dancers who take the lead have to be good tactical thinkers, too, which is why former military officer Bill Scullion, whom you met in Chapter 1, sees partner dancing as an excellent pastime for soldiers:

Bill: They offer Ballroom at the Army Staff College in Leavenworth as an optional activity. It's great for officers who are being reunited with their wives. It used to be required because it's great for posture, and it forces you to think on your feet while moving fast, and maneuvering around other people

to a particular set of standards...all while you're taking care of somebody else. That's what military officers do...they care for their people while they're moving to engage the enemy. Dancing is probably the best activity I can think of to teach you to engage your brain while doing something physically demanding.

Anton Marx, and his wife, Cherella, told me a story that illustrates Bill's point perfectly:

Anton: *I was in a wonderful old ballroom – the Valencia in York, Pennsylvania – doing a solo routine [which means there was only one couple on the floor], and I was going to show everybody that I was Fred Astaire...but what I had not realized was that a staircase going up to the stage intruded on the dance floor.*

So we're going like mad around the floor, and just when I get to my flashiest move, there was this stairway right in front of me. I had to make a sharp turn around the stairway and still get my move in – 'cause I'd memorized this routine.

I barely got through the move when I looked up, and saw a cameraman on the dance floor...with his great big movie camera pointed right at my face...and I had a mind-wipe. I finished the routine, though – just not the way it had been choreographed.

Cherella: *Our teacher said that was a turning point in Anton's dance life, because he'd been able to finish the routine, and make it look good.*

She knew we'd broken the routine, but she was good with that. She said it was excellent that Anton didn't just stop dancing – when he lost his place – and walk off the floor.

One more thing, straight guys: if you want to be an absolute babe magnet, lace up your dancin' shoes. Scientists have finally come up with solid evidence that women are attracted to men who are good dancers.

It's been demonstrated scientifically that women watch good dancers longer than poor ones, and rate them as more masculine and attractive, too.[92] That women pay attention to men who move well to music, and find them attractive, may explain why for thousands of years, males in many cultures have used dancing as a means of attracting mates.

Women can also make accurate inferences about a man's physical strength – and even his personality! – by watching him dance.

Men whose dancing is rated highly by women have been found to have superior hand-grip strength in comparison with men whose dancing is rated lower. Even more surprising, guys whose movements are rated *most* favorably by women tend to score high in the personality traits conscientiousness and social agreeableness.[93]

Finally, it seems women can also accurately estimate a given male's propensity for risk-taking – a trait known to be attractive to women – simply by watching him dance.[94]

Being a diligent researcher, I also searched for anecdotal evidence that girls tend to go for guys who can dance. I typed the question "Do girls like guys who can dance?" into Google...and found only comments in the affirmative. Here's the first four responses listed:

---

[92] Weege, B., Lange, B. & Fink, B. (2012). Women's visual attention to variation in men's dance quality. Personality and Individual Differences, 53(3).
[93] Fink, B., Weege, B., Flugge, J., Roder, S., Neave, N. & McCarty, K. (2012). Personality and Individual Differences, 52(2).
[94] Hugill, N., Fink, B., Neave, N., Besson, A., Bunse, L. (2011). Personality and Individual Differences, 51(4).

1. *Yeah, I think most girls like a guy that can dance*
2. *...um, sure, I guess. It's not the end of the world if he can't dance, but it's fun if he can*
3. *I, being a female, think that it is VERY sexy if a man can dance.*
4. *Heck YESS!!!*

There you have it, fellas. Women *dig* guys who can dance... and hey – the girl of your dreams may be willing to overlook a few shortcomings if you'll accompany her onto the floor. Still don't believe me? Check this out: www.wantromancelearntodance.com

Still not convinced? Take a look at www.dancebetternow.com by Clint Steele – is that a macho name, or what? Clint is a Ph.D. engineer and has a lot of guy-focused material on his page. Even better, he says dance moves remind him of martial arts.

Thanks, Clint. I needed that.

I CAN'T AFFORD IT

I'm going to cut you some slack regarding this one – but not much. I do realize many people are on a tight budget. That being said, there are all kinds of places that offer very reasonably priced dance lessons. At one studio in my area, a 50-minute group lesson followed by a 90-minute party costs $8.00. Eight dollars! That's a *terrific* price for a nice evening out that includes learning something, getting exercise and socializing. In most locations, a movie – at which you'll sit on your butt for two hours – costs more.

Have you thought about what you could maybe give up in order to work dancing into the budget? How 'bout packing lunch instead of buying it? Giving up the smokes? Or, maybe you could do some bartering with a private teacher or folks who run a studio or club. Where there's a will, there's often a way.

The bottom line is that you have to decide to give dancing a chance – and then do whatever you have to do in order to make that happen.

When I was still fat, bored and well on my way to ill-health, how do you think I would have responded had a certain genie popped out of a certain lamp and said:

Marian, I have it in my power to change you into a slim, fit, woman who's back in love with life...but it'll cost ya.

I'll tell you how I would have responded. I would have said this:
I don't care what *it costs. I want that more than* anything!
And then, I would have done whatever I needed to do to pay for it.
Can *you* make that choice?
Remember: Dancin' is for *everyone*! Dogs included![95]

One Last Thought

Dancing is enjoyed and loved all around the world, as shown by the charming, heart-warming video, *Happy People Dancing on Planet Earth:* http://apod.nasa.gov/apod/ap120710.html I challenge you to watch it without smiling!

Consider this observation from Annie LaMotte's gem of a book *Help, Thanks, Wow: The Three Essential Prayers*:

---

[95] Watch the Golden Retriever Merengue video at: http://sorisomail.com/partilha/74298.html

If we stay where we are, where we're stuck, where we're comfortable and safe, we die there. We become like mushrooms, living in the dark, with poop up to our chins. If you want to know only what you already know, you're dying. You're saying: Leave me alone; I don't mind this little rathole. It's warm and dry. Really, it's fine. When nothing new can get in, that's death. When oxygen can't find a way in, you die. But new is scary, and new can be disappointing, and confusing — we had this all figured out, and now we don't. New is life.

If you're reading this book (unless some zealot like me is forcing you to at gunpoint) dancing holds a kernel of interest. Is that because your inner wisdom knows dancing could be right for you? That it could be just what you need to shift your life into high gear? Might *you* find in *your* studio the joy, connection and challenge that I – and the people you've met in this book – have found in *ours*?

There's only one way to find out!

P.S. "Ricardo" asked me to pass this message along to you:

If you're one of those people sitting on the fence, JUST DO IT! It's done so many positive things for me. Things I never expected.